POLYESTERS
VOLUME 1

EDITOR ENGINEERING SERIES
R. M. OGORKIEWICZ
M.Sc.(Eng.), A.M.I.Mech.E.

EDITOR CHEMISTRY SERIES
PROFESSOR P. D. RITCHIE
Ph.D., B.Sc., F.R.I.C., F.R.S.E., F.P.I.

POLYESTERS

VOLUME I
SATURATED POLYMERS

I. GOODMAN, PH.D., M.SC.

and

J. A. RHYS, M.SC., A.R.I.C., F.P.I.

PUBLISHED FOR THE PLASTICS INSTITUTE

LONDON   ILIFFE BOOKS LTD

NEW YORK   AMERICAN ELSEVIER PUBLISHING COMPANY INC.

First published 1965
© *The Plastics Institute* 1965

Published for The Plastics Institute
6 Mandeville Place, London, W.1.
by Iliffe Books Ltd., Dorset House, Stamford Street
London, S.E.1

Published in the U.S.A. by
American Elsevier Publishing Company Inc
52 Vanderbilt Avenue, New York, N.Y. 10017

Library of Congress Catalogue Card Number 65-24350

Printed and bound in England by
The Chapel River Press Ltd
Andover, Hants

BKS 5055

CONTENTS

PREFACE

This volume continues the series of Monographs published during recent years under the aegis of the Plastics Institute. Some aspects of polyester science and technology have, of course, been briefly touched upon in previous Monographs: but the whole polyester field is dealt with here more intensively and in depth.

The Monograph appears in two parts. This book is Volume 1, and covers the linear saturated polyesters. Volume 2 will, in the first place, deal with polyesters which form cross-linked macromolecular net-works, arising for the most part from initially linear but unsaturated polyesters, and in the second place with polyesters whose main application lies in their ability to act as plasticisers for other polymeric systems.

The field of synthetic polyester by now extends over quite a wide range of time: some of them, such as the glyptals, are of a respectable seniority. But, in some parts of the field, the past few years have seen major advances in detailed structural concepts. Our knowledge of the crystallinity and morphology of oriented fibres has become increasingly sophisticated, and has expanded in an exciting manner; and it is, perhaps, in this particular area of knowledge that the main interest of the present volume lies. It is dealt with by Dr. I. Goodman in Chapters 1–5. In Chapter 6, Mr. J. A. Rhys summarises the nature and present status of the polycarbonates, a group of polymers of relatively recent technical interest but of considerable potential for the future.

University of Strathclyde   P. D. R.
March, 1965

ACKNOWLEDGMENT

Chapters 1–5 were written whilst the author was a member of the Research Department of Imperial Chemical Industries Limited, Fibres Division, Harrogate (now incorporated in I.C.I. Fibres Ltd.). He is sincerely indebted to numerous colleagues for discussions and information concerning the properties of many polyesters mentioned in this book, and also to the International Union of Pure and Applied Chemistry and Butterworths Scientific Publications by whose permission Figures 3.13 and 3.14 are printed.

CHAPTER 1

LINEAR POLYESTERS: SOME INTRODUCTORY CONCEPTS

1.1 DEFINITIONS AND NOMENCLATURE

The materials to be considered in Volume I of this Monograph are organic polymers of regular linear structure, characterised by the possession in their repeat-units of ester groups forming integral components of the backbones of the molecular chains. By this definition the linear polyesters are distinguished from such polymeric esters as the cellulose esters, poly(vinyl acetate), and poly(methyl methacrylate), whose ester groups are lateral to the main chains, and also from polymers of branched or netted structure. These distinctions are relevant to the formation and structural integrity of the linear polyesters as well as to their properties and uses. Amongst the whole class of compounds special attention will be given to linear polyesters of crystalline character, many of which can accept, in appropriate conditions, a considerable degree of axial or planar molecular orientation which makes them suitable as synthetic fibre and film-forming materials. Whilst this account will deal in detail with those polyesters which have acquired particular merit in these applications, it will also emphasise the structural relationships of the whole group of compounds in relation to their properties.

Chemically, the linear polyesters can be formulated as the actual or notional products of esterification of diols with dicarboxylic acids, or of the self-esterification of hydroxy-acids, being thus composed of repeat-units of types shown in Fig. 1.1 (a) and (b)).

1

Among synthetic polymers the polyesters have traditionally been categorised together with the polyamides, polyureas, polyanhydrides, and some others as 'condensation polymers', to designate the loss of a molecule of water or other simple substance at each building step in their synthesis and to distinguish them from the so-called 'addition polymers', which contain all of the atoms present

$$[-O\cdot R\cdot O\cdot OC\cdot R'\cdot CO-] \quad [-O\cdot R\cdot CO-] \quad [-O\cdot R\cdot O\cdot CO-]$$

(a)   (b)   (c)

Fig. 1.1

in the monomeric compounds from which they are derived. The ramifications of synthetic method for both classes now make this apparent distinction unreal as well as unhelpful, and the reader is recommended to reserve the term 'condensation' solely for appropriate polymerisation *reactions* as distinct from polymeric *substances*.

Whilst some linear polyesters can be made by the additive polymerisation of monomers (lactones), the group as a whole lacks the names of simple starting materials which can be used with the prefix 'poly' to describe the structures of the high polymers in the same way as polyethylene, polyacrylonitrile, and polybutadiene are named. It is common nomenclatural practice, therefore, to refer to polyesters in terms of the systematic chemical names of their repeat units, e.g. poly(1,2-propylene adipate), poly(ethylene furan-2,5-dicarboxylate), poly(pentamethylene biphenyl-4,4'-dicarboxylate) for Fig. 1.2 (a), (b), and (c) respectively, these names being constructed according to normal practice for simple esters.

As will appear later, the possible range of variance of the groups represented by R and R' is extremely wide, including aliphatic, alicyclic, aromatic, and heterocyclic types, and also encompassing

(a) $[-O.CHMe.CH_2.O.OC.(CH_2)_4.CO-]_n$

(b)

(c)

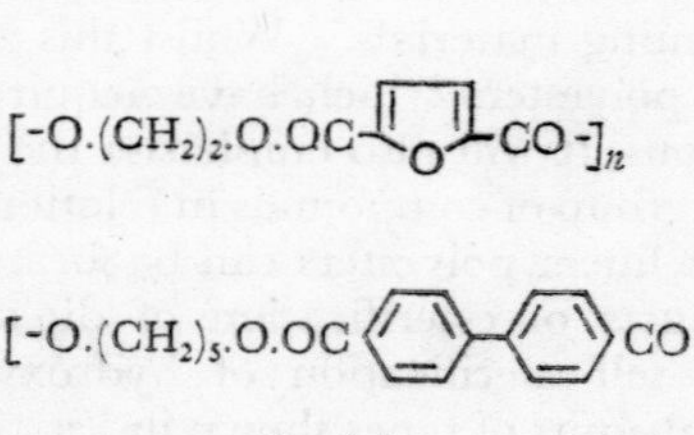

Fig. 1.2

complex units containing nitrogen, phosphorus, sulphur, silicon, or other atoms in the chains, as well as polymeric entities. The polycarbonates, which are polyesters of repeat unit (Fig. 1.1 (c)), fall strictly within the given definition of linear polyesters, and they form a sufficiently distinct sub-group to merit separate discussion (Chapter 6).

Diols and dibasic acids each contain two reactive or functional groups per molecule: and it follows that as the polyester chain-molecule grows stepwise by continued polyreaction, it still bears a functional group at each end of the chain, at each step in its growth. These groups are available for a further reaction step: and this may be of two competitive kinds—*intermolecular*, with extension of chain-length, or *intramolecular*, with cyclisation and cessation of growth. Factors governing this competition will be considered later: for the present it is important to note that where the system contains only difunctional reactants, chain-formation and cyclisation are the only possible modes of reaction. If, however, one or more of the reacting species possesses a functionality higher than two, branched-chain polymers or crosslinked networks can arise.

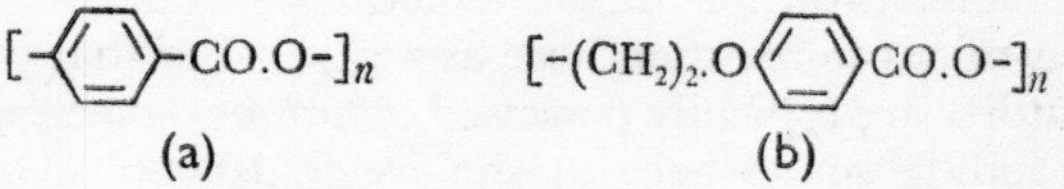

$$[-\langle\!\!\!\bigcirc\!\!\!\rangle\text{-CO.O-}]_n \qquad [\text{-(CH}_2)_2.\text{O}\langle\!\!\!\bigcirc\!\!\!\rangle\text{CO.O-}]_n$$

(a)   (b)

Fig. 1.3

For example, a triol such as glycerol can act as a branching-point in polyesterification: further, if maleic or fumaric acid units are incorporated in the backbone of a linear polyester, the —CH:CH— groups act as additional 'latent' functionalities which can be induced to enter into growing polyvinyl chains, if a monomer such as styrene is added to the system, giving rise to a network. Poly-reactions of this type produce the so-called polyester resins: these are dealt with in Volume II of this Monograph, along with more detailed consideration of the functionality concept which governs their formation.

Some difficulty in nomenclature occasionally arises for polyesters derived from hydroxy-acids, more on account of unfamiliarity than of method. Names such as polyglycollide for $[\text{—CH}_2\cdot\text{CO}\cdot\text{O—}]_n$ and polylactide for $[\text{—CHMe}\cdot\text{CO}\cdot\text{O—}]_n$ that have been applied traditionally to certain of these substances are employed herein, although the more systematic terms poly(methylene carboxylate) and poly(ethylidene carboxylate) are preferable; for others, such as Fig. 1.3 (a) and (b), the self-explanatory terms poly(*p*-phenylene carboxylate) and poly[*p*-(2-ethyleneoxy)benzoate] are superior to the hybrid forms poly(*p*-hydroxybenzoic acid) or poly[*p*-(2-hydroxy-ethoxy)benzoic acid] sometimes employed.

The formulae in Fig. 1.3 may appear at first glance not to correspond in type with the generic formula (Fig. 1.1 (b)) but, on inspection, the sequence of combination of atoms will be seen to be similar, the grouping —CO·O— merely having been emphasised in Fig. 1.3 to conform with the nomenclature proposed. It is often helpful to transpose the parts of polymer repeat-unit formulae in this way to elucidate structural characteristics, provided that care is taken to preserve the correct pattern of succession of groups.

So far we have mentioned only *homopolyesters*—that is, polyesters composed of a single type of constituent unit—but there are also numerous *copolyesters* containing more than one variety of component groups in their molecular chains. There is no settled system for naming the copolyesters of various types which will have to be considered; but, for the simpler types of random copolymers, constructions such as copoly(ethylene isophthalate/terephthalate) (40:60) are reasonably useful, the figures in parentheses being the respective molar ratios of the combined repeat-units.

It is convenient to mention here as a generality that polyesters of practical utility are typically possessed of number-average molecular weights standing somewhere in the range 10,000–50,000, corresponding broadly to degrees of polymerisation of 50–250. Whilst the practical optimum level obviously differs from case to case, this indication will serve to place the size of common polyester molecules in the general context of macromolecular compounds.

1.2 A HISTORICAL PERSPECTIVE

Although the linear polyesters have attained practical importance only within the past thirty years, they have a very much longer history which is partly independent of and partly integral with the history of polymer science itself. Short-chain polyesters of only a few units have long been known to form part of the depsidic constituents of lichens and the tannins of some tree-barks, whilst the polyester [—O·CHMe·CH$_2$·CO—]$_n$ having molecular weights up to some thousands occurs as granules in certain bacteria. Such natural appearances, however, were too sporadic for the early science of organic chemistry to have focussed any serious attention on the compounds as a class. On the other hand, the availability, first of naturally derived polyfunctional alcohols and acids, and later of synthetic members of these classes, led almost inevitably to the production of man-made polyesters, although it was long before these were clearly formulated in this sense. Thus, as early as 1833, Gay-Lussac and Pelouze made what would now be recognised as a polyester from lactic acid, whilst over the period 1847–1901 numerous reports were given of condensation products from glycerol and mannitol with tartaric, citric, sebacic, phthalic, and other acids, work which was later on to bear fruit in the development of the alkyd resins. Also, from 1850 onwards, isolated observations were made on ester-like condensates from the dihydric phenols, from hydroxybenzoic acids, from the salicylides, the 'anhydro-cresotic acids' and others. Early experimenters with the polyesters included such notables as Berzelius, Berthelot, Gerhardt, Schiff, and Anschütz, whilst other contributors, perhaps less well-known, were Einhorn, van Bemmelen, and Lourenço. Attempts were made to assign linear formulae to the polysalicylides by Kraut in 1869, and to the hydroxypivalic polymers by Blaise and Marcilly in 1904, but rationalisation in this field was impossible whilst there was neither any clear picture of the polymeric state nor a recognition that giant molecules could, in fact, exist; indeed, considerable ingenuity was wasted in attempts to picture some of these materials in terms of simple structures of the sort then considered conventional and rational in chemistry. The early history of the subject can be traced in more detail through a number of interesting compilations.[1-4]

So far as the linear-chain polyesters were concerned, this situation persisted into the 1920's, when a variety of independent researches on the nature of cellulose and rubber, on the polyformaldehydes, and on polystyrene led Staudinger, Meyer and Mark, Sponsler and Dore, and others to champion the representation of these materials by covalently bonded linear structures containing recurring identical motifs—the repeat-units. A wealth of evidence was shortly to become available proving the correctness of these hypotheses, and thus confirming beyond any doubt the basis on which polymer science has since relied. A most important part in this resolution was played by the American chemist W. H. Carothers who, from 1928 onwards, undertook the synthesis of linear chain-polymers by known chemical means, selecting the field of polyesters as one of his principal areas of work. Although researches by other workers were simultaneously in progress along analogous lines, the efforts of Carothers and his colleagues were so elegantly and rationally conceived and executed as to provide the most decisive connection of ideas between chemical structure, the polymeric state, and the fibrous condition.

The scope of Carothers' researches can profitably be examined in the original memoirs.[5]   Here note need be taken only of the essential facts—that, by the self-condensation of ω-hydroxy-acids, the polymerisation of certain lactones, or the esterification of linear diols with terminal aliphatic dicarboxylic acids, and provided that steps were taken to force the reactions to give products having molecular weights of above 8,000–10,000, the resultant polyesters were hard solids, crystalline to X-rays, and susceptible to conversion from the molten or dissolved state to filaments, in which form they could be stretched below their melting points, with an ultimate increase in strength, to flexible and tenacious bodies having the properties of true fibres.   An essential conclusion of the work of the time was the recognition that, despite the crystallinity detectable by X-ray methods, well-defined crystals of such polymers could not readily be obtained (indeed, single polymer crystals have only been made within the last few years), and that in general the crystalline entities in polymers were smaller in size than the molecules composing them; from this conception was developed the 'fringed micelle' theory of crystalline polymers, according to which the internal structure is made up partly of crystallite blocks of modest dimensions having chain molecules regularly aligned within them, and proceeding through and beyond them into regions of lesser order where side-by-side molecular regularities may be entirely absent, leading to an amorphous character of part of the material. Although this concept of two-phase texture in crystalline polymers has come into question in recent years, partly through the development of the 'folded molecule' hypothesis and partly through postulations of alternative and more homogeneous forms of defect crystallinity which might exist over the whole bulk of a polymer, no commonly accepted alternative picture of texture has yet emerged, and the older view will be taken for convenience as the starting point for the later discussion.

Fortuitously as it now seems, Carothers' polyesters were mostly of the aliphatic straight-chain type, being in the main materials of low melting point (typically in the range 60–90°C), considerable solubility in organic liquids, and poor resistance to hydrolysis. They therefore lacked promise as sources of textile fibres, and his further efforts on crystalline polymers were turned elsewhere, leading to the discovery in 1935 of the outstandingly successful fibrous polyamide 6·6 nylon.   The polyester story remained to be resumed some years later in England by J. R. Whinfield, whose speculations on the properties to be expected from alterations in the detailed molecular architecture of linear polyesters were confirmed in 1941 by the discovery[6] (with J. T. Dickson) of poly-(ethylene terephthalate), a high-melting compound which proved to have exceptional value as a fibre and film-forming material, and which currently dominates the whole field of linear polyester substances. Since that date, research in the field has been widespread in industrial and academic laboratories in many countries, and the number of polyesters and copolyesters described in the literature—mostly in patent specifications—now amounts to many thousands. Included in this growth of knowledge are the polycarbonates (Chapter 6) and more complex compositions such as the polyesteramides, the block copolyesters, and the polyester rubbers, of which a brief account will be given later; the polysulphonates and polyphosphonates, whose study has commenced in recent years, can also be regarded as being in historical propinquity to their carboxylic analogues. Concurrently with this preparative work and the industrial development resulting from it, considerable effort has been devoted to the elucidation of the molecular and structural characteristics of selected members by the use of the most powerful and sophisticated techniques available to the scientist; their behaviour is now understood to a considerable degree.

1.3   PRESENT STATUS AND AN OUTLINE OF PROPERTIES AND USES

Whinfield and Dickson's discovery, which opened the way to the beneficial utilisation of linear polyesters, was followed, as soon as recovery from wartime circumstances allowed, by an intensive evaluation of the potentialities of poly(ethylene terephthalate) (Fig. 1.4 (a)), and then by its industrial development and production. Rights for the use of the discovery, which was made in the laboratories of The Calico Printers Association Limited, were sold originally to E. I. du Pont de Nemours and Company in the U.S.A. and licensed to Imperial Chemical Industries Limited in England, whose polyester fibres are made under the registered trade names of Dacron and Terylene, respectively; later arrangements permitted the production of similar materials by manufacturers in other countries, these now including Fortrel and Vycron (U.S.A.), Terylene (Canada), Tergal (France), Diolen and Trevira (West

Germany), Teriber (Spain), Terital (Italy), Terlenka (Holland), Tetoron (Japan), Silon-Extra (Czechoslovakia), and Elana (Poland). Fibres of poly(ethylene terephthalate) are also made in the U.S.S.R. under the name Lavsan and in East Germany as Lanon.   Including some copolymers and other minor variants of poly(ethylene terephthalate), the world production of these fibres was estimated to amount to 450 million pounds in 1962.

Of many other polyesters which are fibre-forming, only one is known to have reached commercial production.   This material,

(a) $[-O.(CH_2)_2.O.OC\langle\ \rangle CO-]_n$

(b) $[-O.CH_2\langle\ \rangle CH_2.O.OC\langle\ \rangle CO-]_n$

Fig. 1.4*

* Henceforth throughout Volume I the symbol ϕ will be used for brevity to represent the *p*-phenylene group.

first described[7] in 1955, was a form of poly(cyclohexane-1,4-dimethylene terephthalate) (Fig. 1.4 (b)) having about 70% of the alicyclic rings in the *trans* configuration.   Fibres of this substance were manufactured by the Eastman Kodak Company under the name Kodel, and plans have been announced for it to be offered in West Germany as Vestan; however, poly(ethylene terephthalate) fibres have apparently recently been introduced as Kodel III and IV, leaving the status of this trade name somewhat uncertain.   To avoid confusion in this Monograph, therefore, the name will be used to refer only to fibres of the formula shown in Fig. 1.4 (b).

It is convenient to note here that, in the definition established by the U.S. Federal Trade Commission, a polyester fibre is a manufactured fibre in which the fibre-forming substance is any long-chain synthetic polymer composed of at least 85% by weight of an ester of a dihydric alcohol and terephthalic acid.

Although the properties of polyester fibres will be discussed later in some detail, it is convenient to present here a summary of their leading characteristics and uses with special emphasis on those products likely to be met by the British reader.   Terylene fibres are supplied both in continuous-filament yarn and staple-fibre forms in various deniers (the denier being a function of fibre diameter), lustres, and staple lengths.   The continuous-filament yarns are made in medium and high tenacities with correspondingly different extensibilities to break, whilst the staple fibre, which is normally crimped, has approximately the same tenacity as medium-tenacity filament yarn but possesses different characteristics of extension. The fibres are normally circular in cross-section, although other profiles can be made. Kodel is currently available only in staple-fibre form. The principal tensile properties of these materials are given in Table 1.1 together with comparative figures for some other fibres, the tenacities being expressed in the conventional textile units of grams per denier (1 denier = the weight in grams of 9,000 metres); the newer representation in grams per decitex (1 Tex = the weight in grams of 1,000 metres), which is

Table 1.1 TENSILE PROPERTIES OF SOME POLYESTER AND OTHER FIBRES

Fibre	Tenacity (g/den.)	Extension at break (%)	Initial modulus of elasticity (g/den.)
Terylene (high tenacity)	6·0–7·0	6–14	110–130
Terylene (medium tenacity)	4·0–5·0	15–30	100–115
Terylene (staple fibre)	4·0–5·0	30–50	30–60
Kodel	2·5–3·0	24–30	25–35
Nylon (high tenacity)	6·0–9·5	16–26	65–80
Nylon (medium tenacity)	4·5–5·8	25–35	40–60
Cotton	2·5–5·0	5–10	40–80
Wool	1·2–1·6	30–45	24–40
Acrylic fibres	2·0–3·5	25–45	40–50
Polypropylene	5·0–9·0	15–25	about 90
Silk	3·0–5·0	20–25	60–80
Viscose rayons (normal)	2·0–3·8	17–25	about 65
Viscose rayons (high tenacity)	6·0	6–8	about 170
Cellulose acetate	1·3–6·0	5–30	29–42
Poly(vinyl alcohol) (normal)	3·5–6·0	15–35	15–45

recommended by the International Standards Organisation, can be derived by dividing the given values by 1·11.

Polyester fibres are endowed with an interesting combination of physical and chemical properties, amongst which the following are noteworthy.

1. A hydrophobic nature (the moisture regain at 65% relative humidity and 20°C being below 0·5%) which allows their mechanical performance to be virtually unaffected by the presence of water.
2. Excellent resistance to the action of most organic solvents and many chemical reagents, particularly acids.
3. Indifference to moths, mildews, and micro-organisms.

4. Excellent resistance to tendering by light and general weathering conditions.
5. Good recovery from bending or stretching, low creep, and considerable retention of properties at elevated temperatures.
6. Ability to take a permanent set under the influence of heat.

Their versatility as textiles is displayed both in clothing and in the so-called industrial uses. Terylene staple fibres are thus familiar alone or as blends with wool, cotton, linen, or rayon in suitings, dress, and rainwear fabrics, and in tie-fabrics; bulked-yarn forms are employed in jersey-knitted fabrics and hand-knitting yarns; and continuous-filament yarns are converted to lingerie, lace, curtain fabrics, and similar products. In these uses the advantages of the good weight/strength relationship, the ease of washing, and the capacity to accept permanent pleats with rejection of unwanted creases are seen. The extensive uses other than clothing include sewing threads, ropes, tarpaulins, reinforcements for conveyor belting, fire and fuel hose, ventilation ducting, filter fabrics, safety belts, laundry calenders, dyebags, webbing, electrical cable insulation and bradings, paper-machine felts, and many others; polyester fibres are currently under extensive development in the U.S.A. as cords for vehicle tyres, and similar application is likely to be seen in Europe.

The same combination of properties is also employed to advantage in oriented films made of linear polyesters which are becoming well known in a variety of specialised applications for which the traditional film materials are not suitable. The leading role in this field is again played by poly(ethylene terephthalate), films of which are manufactured by I.C.I. Ltd. in the United Kingdom under the registered trade mark Melinex, and by the du Pont Company in the U.S.A. as Mylar and Cronar. It is also available elsewhere as Hostaphan (West Germany), Montivel (Italy), Terphane (France), and Tetron, Luminar or Diafoil (Japan); the American products Videne and Estar are probably also composed of poly(ethylene terephthalate). Aside from the polycarbonates which are also important in film form, the field as presently constituted is completed with reference to film made of the polyester (Fig. 1.4 (b)) which was first introduced in the U.S.A. as Terafilm but which is now to be made by the Eastman Kodak organisation under the name Kodar.

Melinex film is tough, transparent, and flexible with properties of low water absorption and dimensional stability similar to those of the polyester fibres; it is likewise resistant to oils, fats, and many chemicals, and has a very low permeability to gases and odoriferous substances. It is offered in two types, O and S, of which the former is highly transparent and the latter slightly hazy but with improved slip or handling characteristics, and is available in a variety of widths and gauges. Typical mechanical and electrical properties for 100-gauge film are shown in Table 1.2. These characteristics are exploited in a wide range of uses. Prominent amongst these are the electrical applications, where the film is suitable for electrical capacitors, for electrical motor slot-liners

Table 1.2 SOME PROPERTIES OF 'MELINEX' POLYESTER FILM (100-GAUGE)

Tensile strength	27,000 lb/in^2
Elongation at break	70%
Yield strength	13,000 lb/in^2
Elongation at yield	approx. 5%
Elastic modulus	500,000 lb/in^2
Folding endurance (M.I.T. test)	231,000 cycles
Dielectric constant, 1 kc, 25°C	3·1
Dielectric strength, 25°C	average 4,000 volts
Power factor, 1 kc, 25°C	0·006
Volume resistivity, 25°C	approx. 10^{19} ohm cm
Flexibility	retained down to − 70°C
Shrinkage for balanced film at 200°C for 1 minute	6% in machine and transverse directions

(alone or laminated with paper or with flake mica), and for wrapping and other insulation applications for cables, coils, and transformers. It is also employed in adhesive and magnetic recording tapes; in hose-linings, gaskets, spacers, pump diaphragms, typewriter ribbons, and specialised packaging materials. Because it is free from plasticisers or other additives, metallisation by the vacuum process is easy, and such metallised polyester films are valuable for decorative purposes, in loudspeaker diaphragms, and in laminates or other forms for panelling and lining in motor car and aircraft construction; unstabilised films can also advantageously be used for heat-shrunk packages for food storage and 'boil-in-the-bag' cooking. On account of the increased cost of polyester films relative to such materials as polyethylene and the cellulose esters, it may be conjectured that they are unlikely to find extensive use in general packaging of a non-critical nature; conversely, the established and the ever-growing applications are fully justified in terms of the taxing demands of the outlets and the special properties of the materials. The most exotic of these applications to date is probably seen in the use of Mylar as the constructional material of the American communications satellite Echo 1 of 1960, and in its similar use in the Stratoscope balloon telescopic system and the Ranger lunar-surface exploration vehicles, where polyester fibres are also to be incorporated in laminated or fabric forms.

The last group of polyester applications requiring notice here is that in which these materials are chemically combined into more complex polymers in the so-called polyester rubbers of the Vulcollan class. This use depends upon the elastomeric nature of aliphatic polyesters or copolyesters, modified through the presence of urethane or other characteristic groups, and it is of minor commercial significance relative to other synthetic rubbers and to the broader spectrum of polyester uses already discussed. Nevertheless, these materials find merit in some automobile industry applications where good abrasion resistance allied to good resistance to oil and petrol are required, and where a relatively poor resistance to hydrolytic degradation is not important; world production of these rubbers amounts, however, to only a few hundred tons a year. By modifications to the chemistry and technology of these rubbers it is also possible to obtain elastomeric fibres having a polyester basis, and whilst it is not clear whether such compositions are included amongst the new synthetic elastic fibres now becoming available to the textile industry, a discussion of these polymers will be included in Chapter 5.

REFERENCES

(1) MARVEL, C. S., and HORNING, E. C., *Organic Chemistry, An Advanced Treatise* (GILMAN, H. ed.) Wiley & Sons, New York, 2nd Edition, Chap. 8 (1943)
(2) FLORY, P. J., *Principles of Polymer Chemistry*, Cornell University Press, Ithaca, New York, Chap. 1 (1953)
(3) BEVAN, E. A., and ROBINSON, R. S., *Synthetic Resins and Allied Plastics* (LANGTON, H. M. ed.): Oxford University Press, London, 3rd Edition, Chap. 9 (1951)
(4) ELLIS, C., *The Chemistry of Synthetic Resins*, Reinhold Publishing Corporation, New York, Chaps. 41 and 42 (1935)
(5) *Collected Papers of Wallace Hume Carothers* (MARK, H., and WHITBY, G. S. eds.), Interscience Publishers Inc., New York, (1940)
(6) WHINFIELD, J. R., and DICKSON, J. T., Brit. Pat. 578,079
(7) KIBLER, C. J., BELL, A., and SMITH, J. G. (Kodak Ltd.), Brit. Pat. 818,157

CHAPTER 2

POLYESTER SYNTHESIS AND MANUFACTURE

2.1 INTRODUCTION

It will be apparent from the précis already given that the number of polyester compounds known greatly exceeds those which have attained, or are likely to attain, any degree of commercial importance. The availability of the larger group is nevertheless valuable in providing comparative data useful for the understanding of polyester behaviour and in the improvement of properties of the technically successful members. For this reason the account of polyester synthesis now to be given will deal with all the available methods, indicating broadly their range and utility, as well as with some details of technical practice.

2.2 POLYESTER SYNTHESIS BY CONDENSATION REACTIONS

Virtually every known method of esterification has been applied to the synthesis of polyesters, whilst in addition many of these polymers have been made by reactions which are without counterpart in the chemistry of simple esters. The simplest source of linear polyesters might appear to be through the esterification of diols with dicarboxylic acids or the self-esterification of hydroxy-acids. In practice this approach is used less often than are the modifications wherein functional derivatives of the alcoholic or acid components are the preferred starting materials; but this cognate group of reactions represents the principal means of access to the polyesters. The direct esterification procedure nevertheless calls for some discussion because of its illustrative value for the field as a whole.

The simplest case, that involving the hydroxyacids, can be represented in the following way:

$$n\text{HO} \cdot \text{R} \cdot \text{CO}_2\text{H} \longrightarrow n\text{H}_2\text{O} + [-\text{O} \cdot \text{R} \cdot \text{CO}-]_n$$

It is accomplished by heating the hydroxy-acids alone or with esterification catalysts or promoters, and is normally facilitated by operating under reduced pressure to remove the liberated water whereby the reaction can be forced towards completion; some examples of hydroxy-acids which have been polyesterified in this way are given in Table 2.1.

Temperatures of up to 250–280°C may be required to complete the reaction and the method is therefore not usable with materials

Table 2.1

Hydroxy-acid	Catalyst or condensing agent	Reference
HO·CH$_2$·CO$_2$H	SbF$_5$	1
HO·CH$_2$·CMe$_2$·CO$_2$H	H$_3$PO$_4$	2
HO·(CH$_2$)$_8$·CO$_2$H	None	3
HO·(CH$_2$)$_9$·CO$_2$H	None, or with Me·ϕ·SO$_3$H	4, 5
HO·ϕ·CO$_2$H	(CF$_3$·CO)$_2$O	6
HO·(CH$_2$)$_n$·ϕ·CO$_2$H($n = 1,2$)	None	7
HO·(CH$_2$)$_2$·O·ϕ·(CH$_2$)$_n$·CO$_2$H($n = 0,1,2$)	None, or with Me·ϕ·SO$_3$H	8

which are readily prone to dehydration (e.g. 2-hydroxypropionic acid) or other side reactions; certain short-chain hydroxy-acids will also esterify by cyclisation to give mono- or dilactones rather than linear polymers.

In the esterification of diols with dicarboxylic acids an element of complication arises. Ideally, a high molecular weight linear polyester should result from the completion of the reaction between equal molecular amounts of the participants:

$$n\text{HO} \cdot \text{R} \cdot \text{OH} + n\text{HO}_2\text{C} \cdot \text{R}' \cdot \text{CO}_2\text{H} \longrightarrow$$
$$2n\text{H}_2\text{O} + [-\text{O} \cdot \text{R} \cdot \text{O} \cdot \text{CO} \cdot \text{R}' \cdot \text{CO}-]_n$$

In favourable cases this is possible. However, any imbalance between the molecular proportions of the reactants, whether caused by insufficient accuracy of initial weighing (which, at the precisions required, is readily possible) or by loss of some amount of one or other reactant by volatilisation or side-reaction, will lead at complete esterification to the formation of a polyester terminated at both ends by either —OH or —CO_2H (depending on which reactant is in excess) and thus—if the stoichiometric discrepancy is substantial—to a polyester of limited chain-length. Whilst the possibility now to be discussed should apply in principle to either contingency, one can utilise the hydroxyl-terminated polymer chain for completion of polymerisation in a way which is not practicable for the carboxyl-ended material, and formation of the latter is therefore to be avoided in practice.

Consider the extreme case of the esterification of a dicarboxylic acid with two (or slightly more) equivalents of a diol. When reaction is complete the product will be a dihydroxy-diester of the general formula $HO \cdot R \cdot O \cdot OC \cdot R' \cdot CO \cdot O \cdot R \cdot OH$. A characteristic property of the ester group is its ability to undergo alcoholysis at elevated temperatures, usually with the aid of catalysts, and when this occurs by reaction between dihydroxy-diester molecules, the result is the formation of a polyester chain, diol being eliminated at each chain-linking step, as shown in Fig. 2.1.

$$HO—R—O \cdot OC—R'—CO \mid O—R—OH$$
$$+ H \mid O—R—O \cdot OC—R'—CO \mid O—R—OH$$
$$+ H \mid O—R—O \cdot OC—R'—CO \mid O—R—OH$$
$$+ H \mid O—R—O \cdot OC—R'—CO \mid O—R—OH$$
$$+ \text{etc.}$$
$$\longrightarrow HO—R—O[OC—R'—CO \cdot O—R—O]_n—OC—R'—CO \cdot O—R—OH +$$
$$+ n\, HO—R—OH$$

Fig. 2.1

This method of forcing the polymerisation of polyesters requires the use of high temperatures and the application of high vacua to remove the diol liberated at each step, but it is readily controllable and is a most important means of regulating molecular weight, not only in laboratory practice and where exact stoichiometry of the reactants cannot be assured but also in technical processes for polyester manufacture. As a practical matter it can be inferred from the above scheme that there is no binding necessity to commence solely with the dihydroxy-diester: as long as hydroxyl-terminated chains are present the possibility of chain-growth by continued alcoholysis subsists, and it is therefore feasible to esterify a dicarboxylic acid with just sufficient above one molar equivalent of a diol to produce an intermediate polymer having —OH ends and then, in a second stage, to increase the chain-length by means of the diol elimination reaction. Of course it is fundamental to this approach that the liberated diol be sufficiently volatile to be removed from the reacting mass. Were this not so, it would remain in the system and would itself alcoholyse chain-ester groups so that polymerisation could not proceed; for this reason the elimination reaction is not suitable for use with extremely involatile diols, for which the direct esterification method or one of the variants shortly to be discussed is preferred. The same reasoning underlies the objection mentioned above to the intermediacy of carboxyl-terminated polyesters. Although these can, in principle, undergo analogous reactions of acidolysis, the liberated *di*carboxylic acids are invariably too involatile to be removable as a means of forcing polyesterification; a variation in which *mono*carboxylic acid is removed will be mentioned below.

The direct esterification process for diol-dicarboxylic acid reactions can thus be regarded as a general method, irrespective of whether the stoichiometric or the two-stage procedure is ultimately used. The range of application is vast, and virtually any stable and reactive diol or diacid may be employed, the exceptions being found in acids which are readily decarboxylated, in phenolic hydroxy-acids and dihydric phenols whose esterification is too slow for advantageous use, in diols having tertiary alcoholic groups which would suffer dehydration at the necessary temperatures, and in some tautomeric diols. Practical procedures are substantially similar to those already quoted for the hydroxy-acids, polyesterification being carried out by heating the reactants alone or with the usual esterification catalysts; compounds such as N-methyl-pyrrolidone[9] or trialkylamines[10] have been reported as unusual but effective aids to direct esterification.

We now turn to polyester syntheses by methods which are functionally equivalent to the direct esterification procedure and which the reader should consider in the light of the foregoing discussion. Prominent amongst these is the variation wherein the dicarboxylic acids are replaced by their dialkyl or diaryl esters which are then reacted with diols according to the general scheme:

$$n \, HO \cdot R \cdot OH + n \, R''O \cdot OC \cdot R' \cdot CO \cdot OR'' \longrightarrow$$

$$2n \, R''OH + [-O \cdot R \cdot O \cdot OC \cdot R' \cdot CO-]_n$$

This procedure is generally applied in two stages, the first being the formation of the dihydroxy-diester followed by the polymerisation of this as already outlined. Because of the nature of the replacement occurring in the first stage, the reaction is commonly termed 'ester interchange'. Advantages of this approach include: (*a*) that many dicarboxylic acids of intractable character, which cannot be purified as such to the level necessary for polymer formation, can be more readily refined in the form of their simple esters which are equally useful for polymerisation; (*b*) that condensation of diesters with dihydric phenols and with certain unreactive diols proceeds more readily than with the acids; (*c*) that carboxylic esters are normally lower melting and more miscible with other reagents than their acids, so that homogeneous reaction mixtures are more readily obtained; (*d*) that since esterifications by alcoholysis have a chemical mechanism different from that of direct condensation, being assisted by basic rather than acid catalysts, it is sometimes possible to polymerise esters of which the free parent acids are thermally or otherwise unstable.

So many dicarboxylic esters have been polymerised with diols in this way that only a specimen enumeration can be given. The types include alicyclic and aliphatic dicarboxylates, aromatic dicarboxylic esters of the benzenoid and naphthalenoid series,[11] esters of di(carboxyphenyl)alkanes, di(carboxyphenoxy)alkanes, di(carboxyphenylthio)alkanes,[12-14] and di(carboxyphenylamino)-alkanes,[15] of furan- and thiophen-dicarboxylic acids,[16,17] of biphenyl-dicarboxylic acid,[18] and of di(carboxyphenyl) sulphone.[19] Such acids, together with their substituted or homologous derivates, may be condensed as alkyl esters with the majority of diols of the glycol class and with certain diols such as propane-1,2- and butane-1,3- or -2,3-diols with little difficulty (see, however, Section 2.5). In general there is little to choose between the various alkyl esters as starting materials, but by the use of phenyl esters some condensations are made possible (for example with dihydric phenols and with the rather unreactive 1,1,3,3-tetramethylcyclobutane-1,4-diol) which cannot otherwise readily be achieved. Polycarbonates may also be prepared[20,21] by the use of diethyl or diphenyl carbonate, and other acids which have been polyesterified through their phenyl esters include oxalic,[21,22] isophthalic, terephthalic, cyclohexane-1,4-dicarboxylic,[23] and dimethylmalonic acids.[24]   Esters of hydroxy-acids may also be polymerised in analogous alcohol-elimination reactions, typical examples being shown in Fig. 2.2.

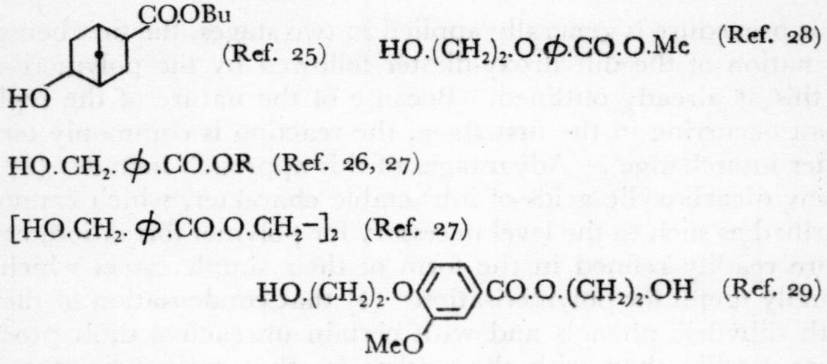

$$HO.(CH_2)_2.O.\phi.CO.O.Me \quad \text{(Ref. 28)}$$

$$HO.CH_2.\phi.CO.OR \quad \text{(Ref. 26, 27)}$$

$$[HO.CH_2.\phi.CO.O.CH_2-]_2 \quad \text{(Ref. 27)}$$

$$HO.(CH_2)_2.O\phi CO.O.(CH_2)_2.OH \quad \text{(Ref. 29)}$$

MeO

Fig. 2.2

The counterpart to ester-interchange polyesterification processes lies in the acid-exchange method, where dicarboxylic acids are reacted with simple diesters of diols or where simple esters of hydroxy-acids are used, the reactions taking the general form of Fig. 2.3.

$$n\,R'\cdot CO\cdot O\cdot R\cdot CO_2H \longrightarrow n\,R'\cdot CO_2H + [-O\cdot R\cdot CO-]_n$$

or

$$n\,R''\cdot CO\cdot O\cdot R\cdot O\cdot OC\cdot R'' + n\,HO_2C\cdot R'\cdot CO_2H \longrightarrow$$

$$2n\,R''\cdot CO_2H + [-O\cdot R\cdot O\cdot OC\cdot R'\cdot CO-]_n$$

Fig. 2.3

This method has been applied to the polycondensation of *p*-acetoxybenzoic acid[30] and is also valuable in the synthesis of polyesters from the diacetates of dihydric phenols;[31] the reaction may be catalysed by small additions of toluenesulphonic acid.   Closely related to it is the use of ethylene and propylene carbonates or of ethylene sulphite[32-34] to form ethylene (or propylene) polyesters by reaction with dicarboxylic acids, carbon or sulphur dioxides being here eliminated as the free 'acid' products (see Fig. 2.4). An interesting extension of this reaction is met when phenolic reactants are used.   Here etherification also occurs so that polyesters

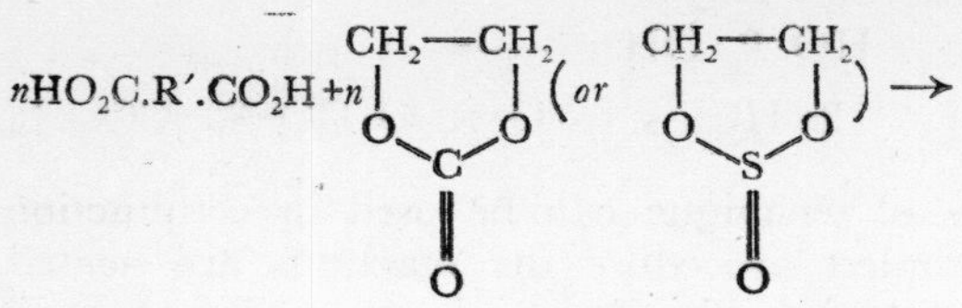

$$nHO_2C.R'.CO_2H + n \left[\begin{array}{c} CH_2\!-\!CH_2 \\ | \qquad | \\ O \qquad O \\ \diagdown C \diagup \\ \| \\ O \end{array} \right] \left(or \begin{array}{c} CH_2\!-\!CH_2 \\ | \qquad | \\ O \qquad O \\ \diagdown S \diagup \\ \| \\ O \end{array} \right) \rightarrow$$

$$\rightarrow [-O.(CH_2)_2.O.OC\text{-}R'\text{-}CO\text{-}]_n + nCO_2(or\ SO_2) + nH_2O$$

Fig. 2.4

of related 2-hydroxyethyl ethers are obtained as in the examples shown in Fig. 2.5.[35]

$$MeO \cdot OC \cdot \phi \cdot OH + \text{ethylene carbonate} \longrightarrow$$
$$MeOH + CO_2 + [-O \cdot (CH_2)_2 \cdot O \cdot \phi \cdot CO-]_n$$

$$HO_2C \cdot \phi \cdot CO_2H + HO \cdot \phi \cdot OH + \text{ethylene carbonate} \longrightarrow$$
$$H_2O + CO_2 + [-O \cdot (CH_2)_2 \cdot O \cdot \phi \cdot O \cdot (CH_2)_2 \cdot O \cdot OC \cdot \phi \cdot CO-]_n$$

Fig. 2.5

What might be termed 'ester metathesis' has also been used to obtain polyesters by elimination of simple esters from fully esterified starting materials as in Fig. 2.6.[36,37]

$$n\, AcO \cdot \phi \cdot CO \cdot OMe \longrightarrow n\, AcOMe + [-O \cdot \phi \cdot CO-]_n$$

$$n\, Me \cdot CO \cdot O \cdot (CH_2)_2 \cdot O \cdot OC \cdot Me + n\, MeO \cdot OC \cdot \phi \cdot CO \cdot OMe \longrightarrow$$
$$2n\, Me \cdot CO \cdot OMe + [-O \cdot (CH_2)_2 \cdot O \cdot OC \cdot \phi \cdot CO-]_n$$

Fig. 2.6

Such reactions are too slow to be of practical value, but closely similar to them—and more effective—is the base-catalysed reaction of diol bis(ethyl carbonates), which yields polycarbonates together with diethyl carbonate[38,39] according to the scheme:

$$n\, EtO \cdot CO \cdot O \cdot R \cdot O \cdot CO \cdot OEt \longrightarrow$$
$$n\, Et_2CO_3 + [-O \cdot R \cdot O \cdot CO-]_n$$

Two further condensation methods of polyester synthesis remain for discussion. The first of these is the reaction of dicarboxylic acid chlorides with appropriate diols, and has the general form:

$$n \ ClCO \cdot R' \cdot COCl + n \ HO \cdot R \cdot OH \longrightarrow$$

$$2n \ HCl + [-O \cdot R \cdot O \cdot CO \cdot R' \cdot CO-]_n$$

Many modifications of technique can be used in conjunction with this. In the simplest procedure the reactants are heated together, alone or in a high-boiling inert solvent or diluent, until reaction is complete. This process may be assisted by passing a current of dry inert gas, such as nitrogen, through the mixture to sweep away the liberated hydrogen chloride. Provided that the reactants are stable in the presence of hydrogen chloride at high temperatures (and some of the lower aliphatic diols, particularly ethylene glycol, are not) this is a satisfactory method of polyesterification, being especially useful with long-chain aliphatic diols[40] and with dihydric phenols.[41]   Suitable solvent or diluent media include high-boiling hydrocarbons, *o*-dichlorobenzene, and the polychlorinated biphenyls (Aroclors), and owing to the normal resistance of ester groups to attack by anhydrous hydrogen chloride, this method of condensation may be applied to diols already containing ester groups, such as di-2-hydroxyethyl terephthalate[42] or hydroxyl-terminated short-chain polyesters,[43] thus providing a source of alternating or block copolyesters.

Alternative to the direct high-temperature process is the reaction of diacyl chlorides with diols in the presence of substances which neutralise the liberated hydrogen chloride immediately on formation, and which may additionally promote the rate of reaction by conversion of the alcoholic groups of the diol to their anions, which are the effective reaction intermediates. This variation, which is of very wide scope and utility, will be treated here only in outline since several excellent reviews and publications cover the subject in detail.[44-49]   Briefly, the whole reaction may be conducted in an organic medium by combining the two reactants in the presence of a tertiary base such as pyridine or dimethylaniline, or the absorption of hydrogen chloride may be effected by the use of aqueous sodium hydroxide, the organic reactants being used alone or preferably with a water-immiscible solvent. Depending on the properties of the products, polyesters are obtained either as precipitated powders or as solutions in the organic solvent which then has to be evaporated to recover the polymer. The reaction of aqueous alkaline solutions of dihydric phenols (for which the reaction is particularly suitable) with the solutions of diacyl chlorides in such solvents as methylene dichloride, chloroform, chlorobenzene, or toluene is assisted by vigorous stirring, which breaks up the water-immiscible phase into fine droplets at whose surface condensation occurs at normal temperatures with extreme rapidity. The dispersion process, which can be promoted by the addition of traces of ionic surfactants, can, in suitable cases, yield polyesters of very high molecular weight more easily than any other condensation method and, for obvious reasons, is now commonly termed 'interfacial polycondensation'. Because of its avoidance of high temperatures, this method of polyesterification is applicable to substances which would not survive the more extreme conditions of all the reactions described heretofore; an example lies in the formation of polyesters from isocinchomeronyl chloride (pyridine-2,5-dicarbonyl chloride) which are not otherwise accessible owing to the thermal instability of pyridine carboxylates.[50]

An important instance of the acid halide-diol reaction carried out in the presence of an acid acceptor occurs in the formation of polycarbonates, the dihalide here being phosgene.[51,52] For this reaction, as with dicarboxylic acid chlorides generally, the acidity of aliphatic diols (i.e. their tendency to form anions) is too low to give useful rates of reaction in the aqueous alkaline system, although the homogeneous pyridine method may be used. A closely related reaction (see also Chapter 6), to which the same considerations apply, is the formation of polycarbonates from diols and preformed bischloroformates,[53,54] of which Fig. 2.7 is an example.

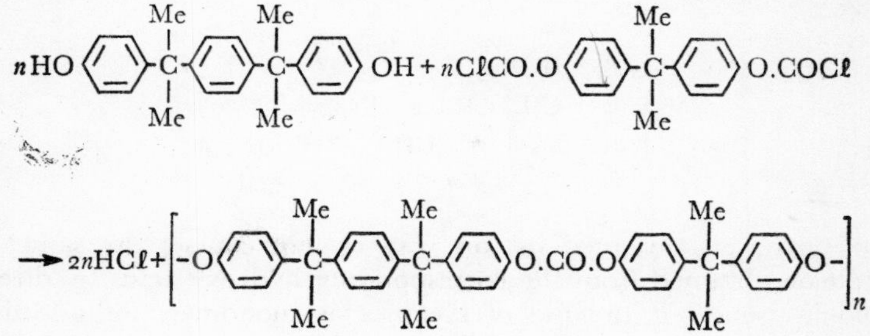

Fig. 2.7

The last condensation process for discussion is that in which dicarboxylic acid salts are the reactive species. Reference was made earlier to the use of lactam or amine assistants in the condensation of acids with diols. These may, in fact, exert their effects through salt formation; but a more pointed instance occurs in the formation of poly(ethylene terephthalate) directly from ethylene glycol and the diammonium or bistriethylammonium salt of terephthalic acid without other catalyst.[55] Polyesters have also been obtained by heating alkylene or xylylene dihalides with the silver, sodium, or potassium salts of dicarboxylic acids,[56-58] and similarly from the salts of halogenocarboxylic acids.[17,59] Although this method has been used to prepare some polyesters, e.g. [—O·CPh$_2$·CO—]$_n$,[60] which are otherwise difficultly accessible, it is too erratic and uncontrollable to be of general utility.

2.3   POLYESTER SYNTHESIS BY ADDITION REACTIONS

The synthetic methods to be considered in this section cover a variety of addition reactions where polyesters are formed from one or more reactants without loss of any of the atoms of the starting materials.

From a practical standpoint the most important of these methods is the polymerisation of cyclic esters or lactones, the simplest examples being those lactones which contain only one ester group in their structures (Fig. 2.8).

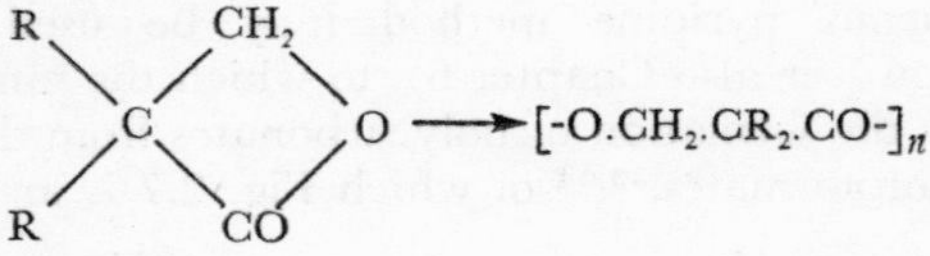

$$R,R = H \text{ (Ref. 61)}$$
$$R,R = CH_3, CH_2C\ell \text{ (Ref. 62, 63)}$$
$$R,R = \text{alkyl } or -(CH_2)_n-\text{(Ref. 64)}$$

Fig. 2.8

The polyesters obtained in this way are, of course, the same as could be obtained from the corresponding hydroxy-acids by direct condensation, but the use of lactones as monomers for additive polymerisation frequently has the merit of proceeding at moderate or low temperatures, thus avoiding the more severe conditions of esterification or ester-exchange which could promote the chemical decomposition of sensitive starting materials.

The study of the readiness of lactones of various structures to polymerise formed a large part of Carothers' early work on polyesters and the subject has been so extended by various workers, notably by Hall and his colleagues,[65-68] that only a brief résumé can be given here. The β-propiolactones just formulated are examples of simple lactones which polymerise with great ease on account of the strain existing in the 4-membered ring. With increase in ring-size, or when the lactones contain more than one ester group in each ring, the rate of polymerisation, or even its occurrence, is very dependent upon the details of chemical structure. Some compounds, illustrated in Fig. 2.9, such as cyclic ethylene oxalate (a), δ-valerolactone (b), or trimethylene carbonate (c), polymerise with great ease or even spontaneously; glycollide (d; R=H) and lactide (d; R=Me) require the use of catalysts and/or

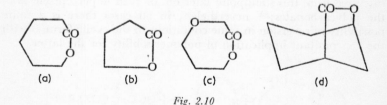

Fig. 2.9

elevated temperatures,[69-71] and some others cannot be polymerised at all—γ-butyrolactone, ethylene carbonate, tetramethylethylene carbonate, γ-valerolactone, and *trans*-hexahydrophthalide. In general, 4-, 7- and 8-membered ring lactones polymerise without difficulty; but among the 5- and 6-membered cyclic esters the effects of substituents, of replacing methylene groups in

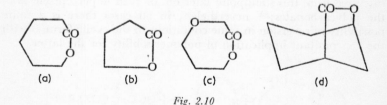

Fig. 2.10

the rings by oxygen, and of other cyclic components of the molecules have an important influence on the reactivity. Thus, whereas ε-caprolactone (Fig. 2.10 (a)) does and γ-butyrolactone (Fig. 2.10 (b)) does not polymerise, the related lactones (Fig. 2.10 (c) and Fig. 2.10 (d)) show a reversed order of reactivity, being respectively non-polymerisable and polymerisable. (*p*-2-Dioxanone, the lower ring homologue of Fig. 2.10 (c), is also easily polymerised). Instances of quite complex lactones which do polymerise include the di- and trisalicylides and di-*o*-cresotide,[72] as well as the macrocyclic terephthalate esters of ethylene and 3-oxapentamethylene glycols.[73,74]

Most polymerisation reactions of lactones require the use of catalysts, which include such substances as inorganic acids, Friedel-Crafts initiators,[71] tertiary amines[62,63] and metal oxides[70] or hydrides.[65] A series of patents granted to the Union Carbide Corporation provides extensive data on the use of organic or organometallic catalysts together with amine or alcohol initiators for the polymerisation of ε-caprolactones.[75-79]

It will be noted that the products of polymerisation of lactones can be regarded, at least formally, as being derived from the monomers by a valence-bond redistribution. In those cases where ionic or basic catalysts are required to effect the reaction, this view of the transformation is almost certainly too simple; but it has been proposed as the probable actual mechanism of the polymerisation of some 6-membered ring lactones of specially facile reactivity whose polyesters also depolymerise readily to the monomers.[80,81] This is only an exaggerated instance of a general phenomenon, namely the equilibrium which exists in all polyesters between the linear chain and the cyclic monomeric or oligomeric forms. For polyesters of practical value it is hardly necessary to add that the equilibrium lies, even at elevated temperatures, virtually wholly on the side of the linear form, so that the normal content of lactone-like material is small, as in poly(ethylene terephthalate) which will be discussed from this standpoint later on, or even imperceptible as in the polycarbonates;[82] nevertheless, in all cases there is a finite possibility of reversion in some conditions to the cyclic form(s) with the concomitant implication of polymerisability for the latter.

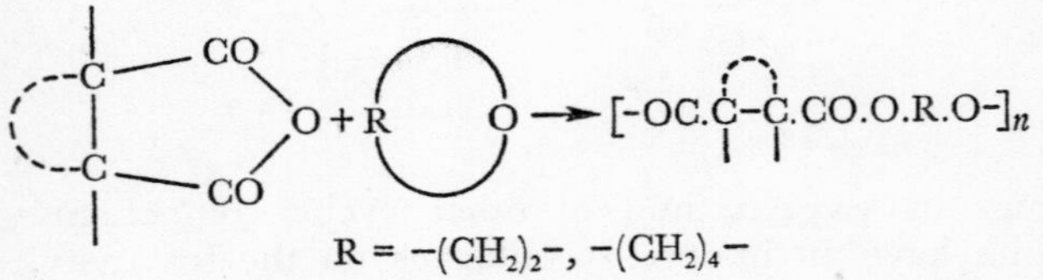

$$R = -(CH_2)_2-, \; -(CH_2)_4-$$

Fig. 2.11

We may now turn to other polyester-forming addition reactions which, being solely of academic interest at the present, will be described only in outline.

The reaction of epoxy compounds with cyclic dicarboxylic anhydrides is an ester-forming process. As described by Austin and Cass[83] and by Fischer,[84] it can be expressed in the general form shown in Fig. 2.11. It has been used to obtain ethylene, 1,2-propylene, and tetramethylene polyesters from such substances as maleic, succinic, and phthalic anhydrides under the influence of tertiary base or Lewis-acid catalysts. Somewhat related is the addition of diols to bisketens,[85,86] which can be regarded as the internal anhydrides of dicarboxylic acids:

$$n \, HO \cdot R \cdot OH + n \, O:C:CH \cdot R' \cdot CH:C:O \longrightarrow$$

$$[-O \cdot R \cdot O \cdot OC \cdot CH_2 \cdot R' \cdot CH_2 \cdot CO-]_n$$

A special case of this occurs in the synthesis of malonate polyesters from diols and carbon suboxide $(O:C:C:C:O)$;[87] these reactions do not require the use of catalysts.

Dimethylketen reacts with aldehydes, ketones, and formate esters to give linear polyester derivatives of substituted β-hydroxy-propionic acids according to the scheme shown in Fig. 2.12, where R is alkyl or aryl, and R' is alkyl, hydrogen, or alkoxy.[88-90]

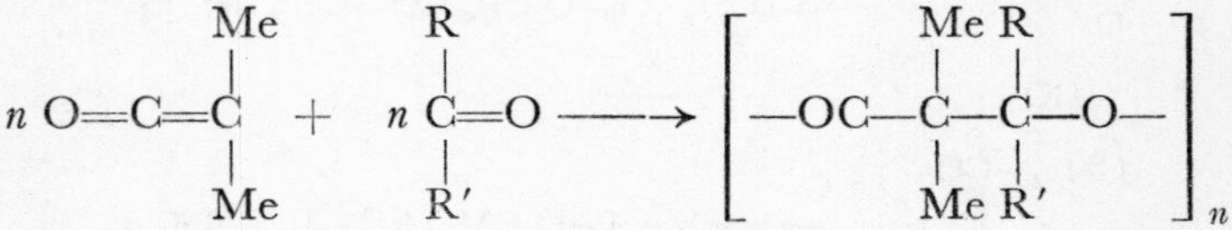

$$n \, O{=}C{=}\underset{\underset{\text{Me}}{|}}{\overset{\overset{\text{Me}}{|}}{C}} \; + \; n \, \underset{\underset{R'}{|}}{\overset{\overset{R}{|}}{C}}{=}O \longrightarrow \left[-OC{-}\underset{\underset{\text{Me}}{|}}{\overset{\overset{\text{Me}}{|}}{C}}{-}\underset{\underset{R'}{|}}{\overset{\overset{R}{|}}{C}}{-}O{-} \right]_n$$

Fig. 2.12

In the last-mentioned case, where formate esters are reactants, the polyesters produced are of the acetal-ester type. These reactions occur under the influence of organo-metallic catalysts such as

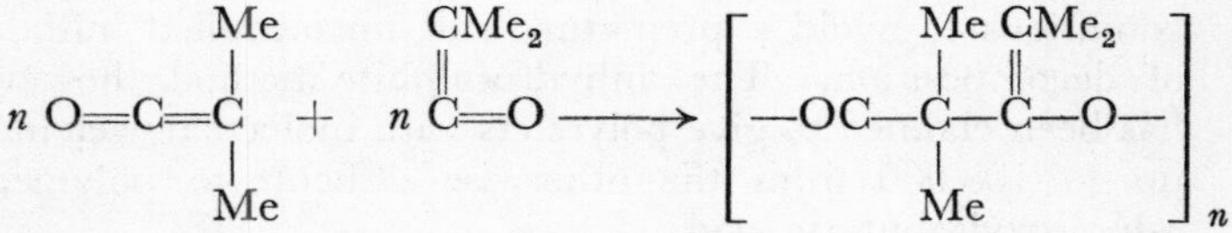

$$n \, O{=}C{=}\underset{\underset{\text{Me}}{|}}{\overset{\overset{\text{Me}}{|}}{C}} \; + \; n \, \overset{\overset{CMe_2}{\|}}{C}{=}O \longrightarrow \left[-OC{-}\underset{\underset{\text{Me}}{|}}{\overset{\overset{\text{Me}}{|}}{C}}{-}\overset{\overset{CMe_2}{\|}}{C}{-}O{-} \right]_n$$

Fig. 2.13

butyl-lithium, and the polymerisation of dimethylketen itself can be directed analogously, by the catalytic action of triethylaluminium, to produce a polyester (Fig. 2.13).[91,92]

Last among polyester-forming addition reactions is the combination of aliphatic or aromatic dicarboxylic acids with diol divinyl ethers; this process, which occurs on heating the reactants together at 150°C, also gives acetal-type polyesters:[93]

$$CH_2 : CH \cdot O \cdot R \cdot O \cdot CH : CH_2 + HO_2C \cdot R' \cdot CO_2H \longrightarrow$$

$$[\text{—}O \cdot CHMe \cdot O \cdot R \cdot O \cdot CHMe \cdot O \cdot OC \cdot R' \cdot CO\text{—}]_n$$

2.4   OTHER POLYESTER-YIELDING REACTIONS

Several other reactions which have been used to produce polyesters remain to be listed.   In general these are more of interest that utility, although some of them might be capable of wider exploitation that has so far been achieved.

1. Cyclic anhydro-esters of carbonic and sulphurous acids with α-hydroxy-acids decompose on heating with the evolution of carbon or sulphur dioxide and the formation of polyesters of the parent hydroxy-acids (Fig. 2.14).

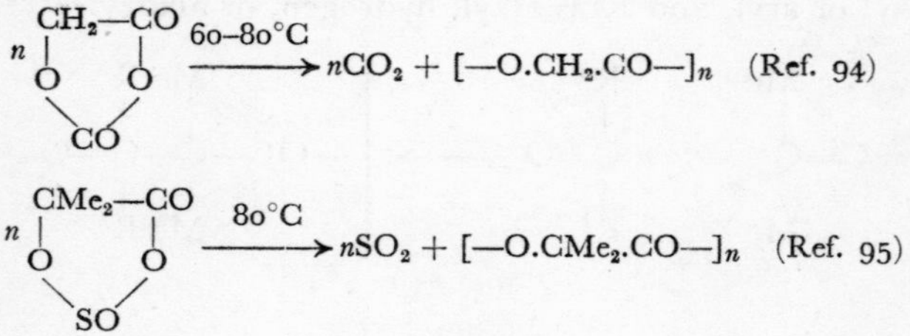

Fig. 2.14

The cyclic esters used in these reactions are obtained by the action of carbonyl or thionyl chlorides upon the α-hydroxy-acids, and it is necessary to maintain strictly anhydrous conditions to avoid a premature and uncontrolled initiation of decomposition.   The anhydrosulphite method, however, has been claimed to give polyesters with molecular weights of up to 108,000 from the otherwise difficult to polymerise α-hydroxyisobutyric acid.

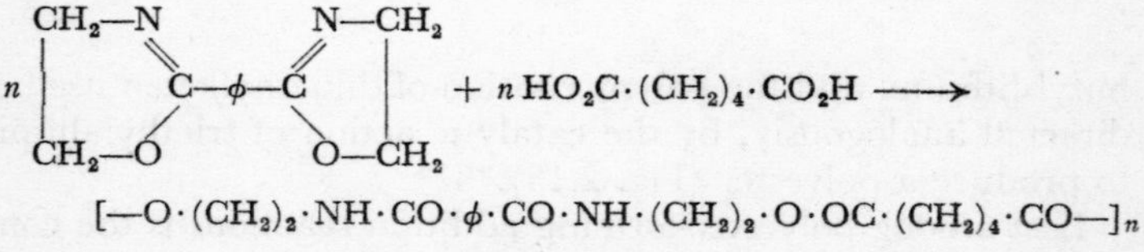

$$[\text{—}O \cdot (CH_2)_2 \cdot NH \cdot CO \cdot \phi \cdot CO \cdot NH \cdot (CH_2)_2 \cdot O \cdot OC \cdot (CH_2)_4 \cdot CO\text{—}]_n$$

Fig. 2.15

2. A polyesterification reaction, actually yielding a polyester-amide, occurs when adipic acid is heated at about 230°C with *p*-phenylene-2,2′-bisoxazoline.[96] (Fig. 2.15). Likewise, a 2,2′-bisoxazolone has been converted to a polyesteramide by reaction with a diol at moderate temperatures[97] (Fig. 2.16).

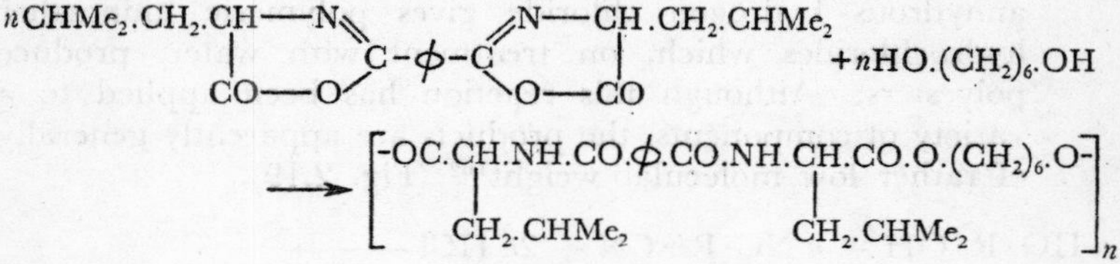

$$n\,\mathrm{CHMe_2.CH_2.CH\!-\!N}\diagdown\!\!\underset{\mathrm{CO\!-\!O}}{\overset{}{\mathrm{C}}}\!\!-\!\phi\!-\!\underset{\mathrm{O\!-\!CO}}{\overset{}{\mathrm{C}}}\diagup\!\!\mathrm{N\!-\!CH.CH_2.CHMe_2} \;\; +n\,\mathrm{HO.(CH_2)_6.OH}$$

$$\longrightarrow \left[\begin{array}{cc} \mathrm{-OC.CH.NH.CO.}\phi\mathrm{.CO.NH.CH.CO.O.(CH_2)_6.O-} \\ \underset{\mathrm{CH_2.CHMe_2}}{|} \qquad\qquad \underset{\mathrm{CH_2.CHMe_2}}{|} \end{array} \right]_n$$

Fig. 2.16

3. The reaction of N,N′-carbonyldiimidazole with dihydric phenols at 40°C in an inert organic solvent provides a source of polycarbonates[98] (Fig. 2.17).

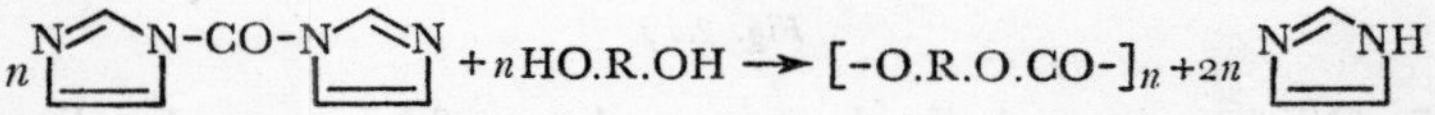

$$n\,\underset{}{\mathrm{N}\diagdown\!\!\diagup\mathrm{N\text{-}CO\text{-}N}\diagdown\!\!\diagup\mathrm{N}} + n\,\mathrm{HO.R.OH} \longrightarrow [\mathrm{-O.R.O.CO\text{-}}]_n + 2n\,\underset{}{\mathrm{N}\diagdown\!\!\diagup\mathrm{NH}}$$

Fig. 2.17

4. Somewhat related to a condensation reaction described earlier is the polyesterification of aliphatic diols and of dihydric phenols with dicarboxylic acid anhydrides.[99,100] The latter are used either as polymeric anhydrides or as mixed anhydrides of the dicarboxylic with a monocarboxylic acid, and

$$[\mathrm{-O\cdot OC\cdot (CH_2)_4\cdot CO-}]_n + n\,\mathrm{HO\cdot\phi\cdot CMe_2\cdot\phi\cdot OH} \longrightarrow$$

$$n\,\mathrm{H_2O} + [\mathrm{-O\cdot\phi\cdot CMe_2\cdot\phi\cdot O\cdot OC\cdot (CH_2)_4\cdot CO-}]_n$$

$$n\,\mathrm{Me\cdot CO\cdot O\cdot OC\cdot\phi\cdot CO\cdot O\cdot OC\cdot Me} + n\,\mathrm{HO\cdot (CH_2)_2\cdot OH} \longrightarrow$$

$$2n\,\mathrm{Me\cdot CO_2H} + [\mathrm{-O\cdot (CH_2)_2\cdot O\cdot OC\cdot\phi\cdot CO-}]_n$$

Fig. 2.18

catalysts such as antimony oxide may be used, the products being water or monocarboxylic acid as well as polyester (Fig. 2.18).

5. The reaction of adipic acid with tetramethylene bischloroformate in the presence of sodium hydroxide and pyridine

has been claimed to yield poly(tetramethylene adipate).[101]

$$n\ HO_2C\cdot(CH_2)_4\cdot CO_2H + n\ ClCO\cdot O\cdot(CH_2)_4\cdot O\cdot COCl \longrightarrow$$
$$[-O\cdot(CH_2)_4\cdot O\cdot OC\cdot(CH_2)_4\cdot CO-]_n + 2n\ HCl + 2n\ CO_2$$

6. The reaction of dinitriles with glycols under the influence of anhydrous hydrogen chloride gives polymeric iminoether hydrochlorides which, on treatment with water, produce polyesters. Although this reaction has been applied to a variety of components, the products are apparently generally of rather low molecular weight[102] (Fig. 2.19).

$$n\ HO\cdot R\cdot OH + n\ NC\cdot R'\cdot CN + 2n\ HCl \longrightarrow$$

$$[-O\cdot R\cdot OC-R'-C-]_n\cdot 2n\ HCl$$
$$\qquad\qquad\overset{\|}{NH}\qquad\overset{\|}{NH}$$

$$\xrightarrow{\text{Hydrolysis}} [-O\cdot R\cdot O\cdot OC\cdot R'\cdot CO-]_n$$

Fig. 2.19

7. Of curiosity only is the reported transformation of a linear polyamide to a polyester by N-nitrosation followed by thermal decomposition:[103] the reaction was accompanied by considerable degradation of the polymer chain.

$$\sim\!\!\sim\!CO\cdot NH\!\sim\!\!\sim \longrightarrow \sim\!\!\sim\!CO\cdot N\!\sim\!\!\sim \longrightarrow$$
$$\qquad\qquad\qquad\qquad\overset{|}{NO}$$

$$[\sim\!\!\sim\!CO\cdot O\cdot N:N\!\sim\!\!\sim] \longrightarrow \sim\!\!\sim\!CO\cdot O\!\sim\!\!\sim$$

8. Lastly, a polymerisation reaction of aromatic dialdehydes under the catalytic action of aluminium ethoxide has been described and formulated as a polyester-forming process.[104]

$$2n\ OHC\cdot R\cdot CHO \longrightarrow [-O\cdot CH_2\cdot R\cdot CH_2\cdot O\cdot OC\cdot R\cdot CO-]_n$$

or

$$2[-O\cdot CH_2\cdot R\cdot CO-]_n$$

The product from terephthalaldehyde is claimed to have a molecular weight of 100,000 or more, and the fact that it yields some terephthalic acid and *p*-hydroxymethylbenzoic acid upon hydrolysis is consistent with a polyester or copoly-ester structure. A complete structural analysis has not been made, however, so that the real value of the reaction is unknown.

2.5 GENERAL REMARKS ON POLYESTER SYNTHESIS

Of the various methods for polyester preparation described above, the most useful are those of direct esterification, ester-interchange, the diol-dicarboxylic chloride reaction, and lactone polymerisation. Some indication has been given already of the classes of reactants for which each is most suitable, and in Section 2.6 further detail will be given of the technical synthesis of the most important polyester, poly(ethylene terephthalate). Here, the general account will be concluded by commenting on some features of polyesterification reactions as they affect particular compounds.

The majority of polyester-forming reactions require the use of considerably elevated temperatures for the inception and continu-ance of polymerisation which will, wherever possible, be carried out without added diluent or solvent so as to facilitate recovery of the product. As with polymers generally, the polyesters once formed cannot readily be purified in the ways possible with simple chemical compounds, and for purely practical reasons it is often difficult to attempt to increase the molecular weight of a polyester which has once been removed from the reaction vessel. It is therefore necessary to aim at conditions most likely to yield products of the required molecular weight with minimum risk of decomposition, or of side-reactions which could complicate the structure of the products or induce the formation of constituents which might hinder the course of polymerisation.

For these reasons, the intermediate chemicals brought to poly-esterification should be of the highest attainable purity, and cata-lysts—where used—should be of such nature and in such amounts as will incur the least risk of inducing undesired side-reactions. The duration of high-temperature polycondensations should be mini-mised by the use, where needed, of reduced pressures and vigorous stirring to assure the quick removal of liberated water, glycols, etc. Blanketing with a dry nitrogen atmosphere is also essential to prevent adventitious oxidation, and indeed, in work on the small laboratory scale, nitrogen may be bubbled through the reacting mixture to provide agitation and a carrier-action for the removal of volatile products. A technique which can be used with advantage to extend the chain-lengths of high-melting polyesters without prolonged exposure to excessively high temperatures is that of powder-polymerisation, in which polycondensation is first carried out in normal melt-conditions until 'prepolymer' of an intermediate degree of polymerisation is formed.   This is cooled and crushed to fine granules or powder which is heated at, say, 200–240°C in a high vacuum (0·01–0·1 mm Hg) for such time as is required to bring the product to the required level of molecular weight by progressive loss of volatile glycol liberated by alcoholysis as described above.   Although such solid-state reactions are slower than the analogous processes in polymer melts, they are sometimes preferable to the latter which are typically conducted in the temperature range of 260–300°C.

Despite these precautions there remain certain peculiarities of reactivity which have to be borne in mind in selecting materials or conditions for making polyesters.   Typical of these is the instability of diols or hydroxy-acids containing tertiary alcoholic groups towards heating or acids; their tendency to suffer dehydration to olefines is so great that polyesters can only be made by special means such as the anhydrosulphite reaction mentioned above. Other difficulties of this sort occur with hydroxy-acids or diols containing a benzyl alcohol grouping ($-C_6H_4 \cdot CH_2 \cdot OH$), and in the polyesterification of trimethylene glycol, both of which are prone to thermal degradation and therefore call for the mildest possible reaction conditions; the degradation of ethylene glycol in esterifications which liberate hydrogen chloride is another instance of a factor limiting the use of a valuable reaction method, and acids containing the grouping $-C_6H_4 \cdot CH:CH \cdot CO_2H$, which readily undergoes decarboxylation to styrene-like products, are best replaced by their esters as sources of the derived polyesters. Another problem arises with difunctional intermediates whose groups have very different reactivities: Cachia and Wahl[105] report an instance of this in 2,6-disubstituted terephthalic acids, one acid function of which, through steric hindrance, is too unreactive to allow normal polymerisation, although the 2,5-disubstituted analogues, having two groups of identical character, undergo polyesterification in a straightforward way.

Stereochemical factors may also play a part in polycondensation reactions.   In the preparation of polyesters from mixtures of the *cis* and *trans* isomers of cyclohexane-1,4-dimethanol, the latter is the more reactive, so that when an excess of glycol over dicarboxylic ester is used, the polyester formed may be richer in *trans*-cyclohexylene content than the original diol mixture;[106] Chien and Walker have also demonstrated the stereoisomerisation of the cyclohexane-1,4-dicarboxylic ester structure in its polyesterification with ethylene glycol at 285°C, the products having an equilibrium isomeric composition of 41% *cis* and 59% *trans* rings even though the pure *cis* or *trans* dimethyl esters were employed as starting materials.[107]

By using mixtures of suitably reactive compounds (e.g. two or more diols with one or more dicarboxylic acids), or of hydroxyacids with diol-dicarboxylic acid mixtures, copolyesters are readily formed. The normal reactions applied to such mixed reactants naturally yield random copolymers which, in number, far exceed the ordered copolymers for which special preparative procedures have to be devised. Copolyesterification is subject to the same limiting considerations as are discussed above for the simpler polyesters; but provided that no change in reactant mixture composition occurs during reaction, they will possess the same molar proportions of structural components as were initially fed. Mixtures of dicarboxylic acids or esters ordinarily conform to this requirement, but when two diols of different volatility are employed, there is a risk of enrichment of the less volatile one in the product. In such cases it may be advisable to forego the practical advantages obtained by working with an excess of diol in favour of reaction with near-stoichiometric proportions of reactants.

2.6 MANUFACTURE OF POLY(ETHYLENE TEREPHTHALATE)

Except for the polycarbonates, the only linear polyesters of practical significance at the present time are those based on terephthalic acid, and an account of the technical production of its ethylene polyester will be given as an example of the application of the principles dealt with above.

Both ethylene glycol and terephthalic acid are products of the chemical transformation of hydrocarbons derived from petroleum. The glycol is produced from ethylene by way of ethylene chlorohydrin or ethylene oxide, and the terephthalic acid used in polyester synthesis is mostly manufactured by the oxidation of *p*-xylene, a product of the fractionation of reformed naphthas. This oxidation is effected in various ways. In one process the reaction of *p*-xylene with air at high temperatures gives *p*-toluic acid, which is converted to methyl *p*-toluate and then oxidised further with air to methyl hydrogen terephthalate; other oxidation processes employed on the large scale include the through-oxidation of xylene to terephthalic acid by means of nitric acid, or with air under the catalytic agency of metal bromides. An alternative oxidation process of an indirect sort converts a gaseous mixture of *p*-xylene, oxygen, and ammonia to terephthalonitrile, which can readily be hydrolysed to the acid. Terephthalic acid can also be obtained by reaction sequences beginning with benzene, toluene, or *m*-xylene, which can thus replace *p*-xylene as raw materials. These routes include the chloromethylation or carbonylation of toluene to *p*-methylbenzyl chloride or *p*-tolualdehyde, respectively, followed by oxidation steps; the thermal isomerisation of alkali-metal salts of benzoic and isophthalic acids to terephthalates is also technically feasible, and the *p*-dicarboxylic acid has also been made by the oxidation of *p*-diisopropylbenzene, a product of the reaction of propylene with benzene.

Whilst poly(ethylene terephthalate) can be obtained by the direct esterification of ethylene glycol with terephthalic acid, technical practice is almost wholly based upon the ester-exchange reaction of the glycol with the dimethyl ester of the acid. The reason for this choice is partly the greater convenience in the early stages of polyesterification given by the lower melting point of the dimethyl ester and its higher solubility in the glycol, and partly the fact that terephthalic acid itself is a rather intractable substance, difficult to purify to the high standards appropriate for polymerisation. The dimethyl ester, on the other hand, can readily be refined by crystallisation or distillation.

The first stage of polymer manufacture consists in heating dimethyl terephthalate with $2 \cdot 1 - 2 \cdot 2$ molar equivalents of ethylene glycol to temperatures in the range $150-210°C$, when, under the action of suitable catalysts, methanol is evolved and there is formed the so-called 'monomer', a mixture consisting mainly of di-2-hydroxyethyl terephthalate, $HO \cdot (CH_2)_2 \cdot O \cdot OC \cdot \phi \cdot CO \cdot O \cdot (CH_2)_2 \cdot OH$, together with some proportion of 'dimer', 'trimer', etc.,—that is to say, of oligomers having the general formula:

$$HO \cdot (CH_2)_2 \cdot O \cdot [OC \cdot \phi \cdot CO \cdot O \cdot (CH_2)_2 \cdot O]_n \cdot H$$

The ester-exchange reaction is reversible, and the liberated methanol is therefore removed through a fractionating column to complete the transformation, which is also assisted by the slight excess of glycol employed; this too is removed by distillation at the end of the first stage. Polycondensation proper is then effected by heating the mixture of glycol esters to a considerably higher temperature, when the alcoholysis process mentioned in Section 2.2 takes place with elimination of ethylene glycol and formation of a high polymer. The growth of the polyester molecules is accompanied by an increase in the viscosity of the molten mixture, and the reaction is terminated when this has reached a value known to correspond with the required molecular weight. The temperature at which polycondensation is carried out must be sufficient to retain the product in molten form so that it can be removed eventually from the reaction vessel; furthermore, because the polymerisation reaction is reversible, efficient removal of the liberated diol is essential. These requirements are met by carrying out the second stage of the reaction at 270–285°C, with continuous evacuation to pressures below 1 mm. Hg.

It is, of course, possible to synthesise di-2-hydroxyethyl terephthalate by means other than the use of dimethyl terephthalate. There has been considerable study of its preparation from terephthalic acid and ethylene oxide or ethylene carbonate, or from disodium terephthalate and ethylene chlorohydrin, with subsequent polymerisation following the normal course; but none of these alternatives appears yet to have been adapted to large-scale manufacture.

The polymerisation process, like the ester-exchange step, requires the assistance of catalysts in order to proceed at an acceptable rate. Such catalysis is provided for both stages by the addition of compounds (oxides, carbonates, alkoxides, or alkanoates) of certain weakly basic or amphoteric metals or metalloids. Whilst many metal compounds show some catalytic activity, those chosen for commercial use provide a favourable balance between the rates of the wanted reactions and those of the undesirable degradation reactions which may also be induced. In the early days of polyester manufacture, a single catalyst, e.g. lead oxide, was employed to promote both stages of reaction, but it has now become more usual to employ mixed catalysts, one component of which is specially active in the ester-exchange step and the other in the polymerisation stage. Practical usage ranges over compounds of magnesium, zinc, cadmium, calcium, strontium, barium, lead, manganese, and cobalt, used separately or together with compounds of antimony, germanium, tin, or titanium.

Many of these substances are suitable catalysts for other polyesterifications—titanium alkoxides, for example, are specially valuable with complex glycols—but little is known at a fundamental level as to their mode of action. Comparative studies of the effectiveness of various metals have been made by various workers[108-110] and an extensive bibliography is to be found in a paper by Wilfong.[111] Mechanistic understanding of the ester-exchange process and of the molecular chain building reaction is likewise only poorly developed; kinetic studies of the glycol-dimethyl terephthalate reaction and of the succeeding stage have been made,[111-115] but the findings of different workers are not in sufficient agreement to be easily summarised.

In the manufacture of poly(ethylene terephthalate) for fibres it is usual to add a small amount of titanium dioxide to the reaction mass to serve as a white pigment or delustrant which confers an attractive matt appearance on the resultant filaments; the normal amount is about 0·5% of the weight of the polymer, though this may be increased or decreased to provide heavier or lighter effects. Phosphorus compounds may also be added to inactivate the catalysts at the end of the reaction, or to prevent their deposition as insoluble salts of terephthalic acid,[116,117] and the introduction of mono-carboxylic esters as 'chain-stoppers' has been proposed[118,119] to assist in the control of molecular weights.

At the completion of polymerisation the vacuum is released and the polyester is discharged from the reaction vessel as a liquid which is cooled rapidly for solidification, after which it is cut up to handle-able 'chips' or flakes which form the starting material for conversion to fibres or films.

REFERENCES

(1) BECK, M. L. (E. I. du Pont de Nemours and Company), U.S. Pat. 2,585,427
(2) ALDERSON, T. (E. I. du Pont de Nemours and Company), U.S. Pat. 2,658,055
(3) LYCAN, W. H., and ADAMS, R., *J. Amer. Chem. Soc.*, **51**, 625 (1929)
(4) LYCAN, W. H., and ADAMS, R., *J. Amer. Chem. Soc.*, **51**, 3450 (1929)
(5) CAROTHERS, W. H., and VAN NATTA, F. J., *J. Amer. Chem. Soc.*, **55**, 4714 (1933)
(6) BOURNE, E. J., STACEY, M., TATLOW, J. C., and TEDDER, J. M., *J. Chem. Soc.*, 2976 (1949)
(7) COOK, J. G., DICKSON, J. T., LOWE, A. R., WHINFIELD, J. R. (Imperial Chemical Industries Limited), Brit. Pat. 604,985
(8) REEDER, F., and WALLSGROVE, E. R. (Courtaulds Limited), Brit. Pat. 641,320
(9) SUBLETT, R. L. (The Chemstrand Corporation), U.S. Pat. 2,719,835
(10) The Chemstrand Corporation, Brit. Pat., 904,446
(11) COOK, J. G., HUGGILL, H. P. W., LOWE, A. R. (Imperial Chemical Industries Ltd.), Brit. Pat. 604,073
(12) COOK, J. G., DICKSON, J. T., HUGGILL, H. P. W. (Imperial Chemical Industries Limited), Brit. Pat. 588,497
(13) DICKSON, J. T., Brit. Pat. 579,462
(14) LOWE, A. R. (Imperial Chemical Industries Limited), Brit. Pat. 604,075
(15) BIRTWHISTLE, W. K., Brit. Pat. 609,792
(16) DREWITT, J. G. N., and LINCOLN, J. (Celanese Corporation of America), U.S. Pat. 2,551,731

(17) HACHIHAMA, J., SHONO, T., and HYONO, K., *Technol. Rept. Osaka Univ.* **8**, 475 (1958) (through Chem. Abstr. **53**, 18933 (1959))
(18) WIELICKI, E. A., and EVANS, R. D. (American Viscose Corporation), Brit. Pats. 884,680; 885,049
(19) CALDWELL, J. R. (Eastman Kodak Company), U.S. Pat. 2,744,089
(20) Farbenfabriken Bayer A.G., Belgian Pat. 546,376
(21) Farbenfabriken Bayer A.G., Brit. Pat. 857,378
(22) Gevaert Photo-Producten N.V., Belgian Pat. 585,556
(23) ELAM, E. U., MARTIN, J. C., and GILKEY, R. (Kodak-Pathé), French Pat. 1,278,284
(24) THIEBAULT, R. P. J. G., and ÉTIENNE, Y. P. M. (Eastman Kodak Co.), U.S. Pat. 3,043,799
(25) CALDWELL, J. R., and JACKSON, W. J. (Eastman Kodak Company), U.S. Pat. 3,000,864
(26) LUDEWIG, H., RAMM, H., and WIEGAND, K., *J. Prakt. Chem.* [4] **6**, 103 (1958)
(27) ZÁMORSKÝ, Z., and VESELÝ, R., *Chem. Průmysl*, **6/33**, 106 (1958)
(28) National Rayon Pulp Company Limited, Jap. Pat. 9598/59
(29) Inventa A.G. für Forschung und Patentverwertung, French Pat. 1,220,725
(30) AELONY, D., and RENFREW, M. M. (General Mills, Inc.), U.S. Pat. 2,728,747
(31) CONIX, A. J. (Gevaert Photo-Production N.V.), Brit. Pat. 883,312
(32) DREWITT, J. G. N., and LINCOLN, J. (British Celanese Ltd.), U.S. Pat. 2,799,667
(33) The Chemstrand Corporation, Brit. Pat. 769,700
(34) Farbwerke Hoechst A.G., Brit. Pat. 781,169
(35) LINCOLN, J. (British Celanese Limited), U.S. Pat. 2,799,665
(36) GLEIM, W. K. T. (Universal Oil Products Company), U.S. Pat. 3,039,994
(37) COOK, J. G. (Imperial Chemical Industries Limited), Brit. Pat. 590,417
(38) REYNOLDS, D. D., and VAN DEN BERGHE, J. (Eastman Kodak Company), U.S. Pat. 2,789,509
(39) GAWLAK, M., PALMER, R. P., ROSE, J. B., SANDIFORD, D. J. H., and TURNER-JONES, A., *Chem. & Ind.* 1148 (1962)
(40) Wingfoot Corporation, Brit. Pat. 627,270
(41) KANTOR, S. W., and HOLUB, F. F. (General Electric Company), U.S. Pats. 3,036,990–992
(42) RASHBROOK, R. B. (Imperial Chemical Industries Limited), Brit. Pat. 898,300
(43) FLORY, P. J. (The Goodyear Tire and Rubber Company), U.S. Pat. 2,691,006
(44) KORSHAK, V. V., and VINOGRADOVA, S. V., *Russ. Chem. Revs.* (English Trans.), **30**, 171 (1961)
(45) EARECKSON, W. M., *J. Polymer Sci.*, **40**, 399 (1959)
(46) CONIX, A., *Industr. Chim. Belge*, **22**, 1457 (1957)
(47) CONIX, A., *Industr. Engng. Chem.*, **51**, 147 (1959)
(48) CONIX, A. J., and LARIDON, U. L. (Gevaert Photo-Producten N.V.), U.S. Pat. 3,028,364
(49) CONIX, A. J. (Gevaert Photo-Producten N.V.), Brit. Pat. 901,605
(50) STIMPSON, J. W. (Imperial Chemical Industries Limited), Brit. Pat. 853,730
(51) Farbenfabriken Bayer A.G., Belgian Pat. 532,543
(52) SCHNELL, H., *Angew. Chem.*, **68**, 633 (1956)
(53) Farbenfabriken Bayer A.G., Brit. Pat. 808,487
(54) SCHNELL, H., FRITZ, G., and BOTTENBRUCH, L. (Farbenfabriken Bayer A.G.), Belgian Pat. 614,664
(55) DICKSON, J. T., HUGGILL, H. P. W., and WELCH, J. C., Brit. Pat. 590,451
(56) Farbenfabriken Bayer in Leverkusen, German Pat. 318,222
(57) CAROTHERS, W. H., and ARVIN, G. A., *J. Amer. Chem. Soc.*, **51**, 2560 (1929)
(58) Pittsburgh Plate Glass Company, Brit. Pat. 815,852
(59) Vereinigte Glanzstoff-Fabriken A.G., Belgian Pat. 538,255
(60) BEZZI, S., *Gazz. Chim. Ital.*, **79**, 219 (1949)
(61) GRESHAM, T., JANSEN, J., and SHAVER, F., *J. Amer. Chem. Soc.*, **70**, 998 (1948)

(62) REYNOLDS, R. J. W., and VICKERS, E. J. (Imperial Chemical Industries Limited), Brit. Pat. 766,347
(63) VICKERS, E. J., and REYNOLDS, R. J. W. (Imperial Chemical Industries Limited), Brit. Pat. 775,495
(64) ÉTIENNE, Y. P. M., and FISCHER, N. (Kodak-Pathé), French Pat. 1,231,163
(65) HALL, H. K., and SCHNEIDER, A. K., *J. Amer. Chem. Soc.*, **80**, 6409 (1958)
(66) HALL, H. K., *J. Amer. Chem. Soc.*, **80**, 6412 (1958)
(67) HALL, H. K., BRANDT, M. K., and MASON, R. M., *J. Amer. Chem. Soc.*, **80**, 6420 (1958)
(68) HALL, H. K., and ZBINDEN, R., *J. Amer. Chem. Soc.*, **80**, 6428 (1958)
(69) LOWE, C. E. (E. I. du Pont de Nemours and Company), U.S. Pat. 2,668,162
(70) SALZBERG, P. L. (E. I. du Pont de Nemours and Company), U.S. Pat. 2,758,987
(71) KLEINE, J., and KLEINE, H-H., *Makromol. Chem.*, **30**, 23 (1959)
(72) SCHNEIDER, A. K. (E. I. du Pont de Nemours and Company), U.S. Pat. 2,696,481
(73) GOODMAN, I., and NESBITT, B. F. (Imperial Chemical Industries Limited), Brit. Pat. 843,356
(74) GOODMAN, I., and NESBITT, B. F. (Imperial Chemical Industries Limited), Brit. Pat. 851,369
(75) YOUNG, D. M., HOSTETTLER, F., and HORN, C. F. (Union Carbide Corporation), Brit. Pat. 859,639
(76) YOUNG, D. M., and HOSTETTLER, F. (Union Carbide Corporation), Brit. Pat. 859,642
(77) HOSTETTLER, F., and SHRIVER, L. C. (Union Carbide Corporation), Brit. Pat. 859,643
(78) YOUNG, D. M., HOSTETTLER, F., and MCLAUGHLIN, R. W. (Union Carbide Corporation), Brit. Pat. 859,644
(79) FOWLER, G. W., and CARRUTHERS, T. F. (Union Carbide Corporation), Brit. Pat. 859,645
(80) STANNETT, V., and SZWARC, M., *J. Polymer Sci.*, **10**, 587 (1953)
(81) SAREL, S., and POHORYLES, L. A., *J. Amer. Chem. Soc.*, **80**, 4596 (1958)
(82) SCHNELL, H., and BOTTENBRUCH, L., *Makromol. Chem.*, **57**, 1 (1962)
(83) AUSTIN, P. R., and CASS, O. W. (E. I. du Pont de Nemours and Company), U.S. Pat. 2,811,512
(84) FISCHER, R. F., *J. Polymer Sci.*, **44**, 155 (1960)
(85) HAGEMEYER, H. J. (Eastman Kodak Company), U.S. Pat. 2,533,455
(86) BLOMQUIST, A. T. (The B.F. Goodrich Company), U.S. Pat. 3,002,024
(87) KORSHAK, V. V., ROGOZHIN, S. V., and VOLKOV, V. I., *Vysokomolekul. Soedin.*, **1**, 805 (1959)
(88) NATTA, G., MAZZANTI, G., PREGAGLIA, G., and BINAGHI, M., *J. Amer. Chem. Soc.*, **82**, 5511 (1960)
(89) NATTA, G., MAZZANTI, G., PREGAGLIA, G., and BINAGHI, M. (Montecatini Società Generale per l'Industria Mineraria e Chimica), Belgian Pat. 600,910
(90) MILLER, R. G. J., NIELD, E., and TURNER-JONES, A., *Chem. & Ind.*, 181 (1962)
(91) NATTA, G., MAZZANTI, G., PREGAGLIA, G., BINAGHI, M., and PERALDO, M., *J. Amer. Chem. Soc.*, **82**, 4742 (1960)
(92) NATTA, G., MAZZANTI, G., and PREGAGLIA, G. (Montecatini Società Generale per l'Industria Mineraria e Chimica), Brit. Pat. 893,308
(93) Deutsche Solvay-Werke G.m.b.H., Brit. Pat. 768,305
(94) DAVIES, W. H., *J. Chem. Soc.*, 1357 (1951)
(95) ALDERSON, T. (E. I. du Pont de Nemours and Company), U.S. Pat. 2,811,511
(96) JAEGER, A. (Farbwerke Hoechst A.G.), Deutsche Auslegeschrift 1,050,540
(97) CLEAVER, C. J., and PRATT, B. C., *J. Amer. Chem. Soc.*, **77**, 1541 (1955)
(98) P. Beiersdorf & Co. A.G., Brit. Pat. 846,044
(99) Gevaert Photo-Producten N.V., Belgian Pat. 549,667
(100) Monsanto Chemical Company, British Pat. 898,301

(101) Badische Anilin- & Soda Fabrik, British Pat., 730,599
(102) ZIL'BERMAN, E. N., and TEPLYAKOV, N. M., *Vysokomolekul. Soedin.*, **1**, 934 (1959); **2**, 133 (1960)
(103) PORTER, M. R., *J. Polymer Sci.*, **33**, 447 (1958)
(104) MITIN, YU. V., SAZANOV, YU. N., VLASOV, G. P., and KOTON, M. M., *Vysokomolekul. Soedin.*, **2**, 716 (1960)
(105) CACHIA, M., and WAHL, H., *C.R. Acad. Sci., Paris*, **247**, 88 (1958)
(106) KIBLER, C. J., BELL, A., and SMITH, J. G. (Kodak Ltd.), Brit. Pat. 818,157
(107) CHIEN, J. C. W., and WALKER, J. F., *J. Polymer Sci.*, **45**, 239 (1962)
(108) ZIMMERMANN, H., *Faserforsch. Textiltech.*, **13**, 481 (1962)
(109) TORRACA, G., and TURRIZIANI, R., *Chim. Ind.*, **44**, 483 (1962)
(110) PETUKHOV, B. V., and TEREKHOVA, G. M., *Khim. Volokna*, 24 (1961)
(111) WILFONG, R. E., *J. Polymer Sci.*, **54**, 385 (1961)
(112) KORSHAK, V. V., BEKASOVA, N. I., and ZAMYATINA, V. A., *Izv. Akad. Nauk S.S.S.R., Otd. Khim. Nauk*, 486 (1958)
(113) CHALLA, G., *Makromol. Chem.*, **38**, 105, 123, 138 (1960)
(114) CHALLA, G., *Rec. Trav. Chim.*, **79**, 90 (1960)
(115) GRIEHL, W., and SCHNOCK, G., *Faserforsch. Textiltech.*, **8**, 408 (1957)
(116) ISAACS, E., and MUNRO, N. (Imperial Chemical Industries Limited), Brit. Pat. 802,921
(117) SCOTT, N. D., and MUNRO, N. (Imperial Chemical Industries Limited), Brit. Pat. 886,966
(118) ALLES, F. P., and SAUER, W. R. (E. I. du Pont de Nemours and Company), U.S. Pat. 2,758,105
(119) FLETCHER, N. (Imperial Chemical Industries Limited), Brit. Pat. 838,663

CHAPTER 3

POLYESTERS AS FIBRE- AND FILM-FORMING MATERIALS

3.1 INTRODUCTION

The technologies of fibre- and film-making from the linear polyesters, and the behaviour of the products, so closely reflect the molecular properties of the polymers that a review of these properties must logically precede the discussion of fabrication methods and of the characteristics of the resultant products. This Chapter will again be devoted mainly to the behaviour of poly(ethylene terephthalate), with occasional reference to other polyesters; but since few of the latter have been studied in detail any comparison of properties must necessarily be somewhat superficial.

3.2 GENERAL AND MOLECULAR PROPERTIES AND STRUCTURE OF POLY(ETHYLENE TEREPHTHALATE)

Poly(ethylene terephthalate) is a colourless material which melts, when crystalline, at about 262–265°C to a colourless viscous liquid. The representation of its chemical structure given earlier in formula Fig. 1.4 (a) represents a simplification of the reality since it takes no account of the end-groups, of the distribution of molecular weights, or of the structural abnormalities resulting from side-reactions of polymerisation; indeed, the *linearly* repeating ethylene terephthalate unit probably constitutes no more than 98% of the weight of commercial samples. The molecular weights of poly(ethylene terephthalate) specimens are most conveniently assessed viscometrically in non-degrading solvents by reference to equations derived from end-group analysis or by fractionation. Equations relating the intrinsic viscosity $[\eta]$ in certain solvents to number-average molecular weight (M_n) take the form $[\eta] = KM_n^{\alpha}$ and values are summarised in Table 3.1 for the constants K and α deduced for this polymer by various investigators.

Table 3.1

Solvent	K	α	References
Phenol-tetrachloroethane	$1 \cdot 27 \times 10^{-4}$	$0 \cdot 86$	1
o-Chlorophenol	$1 \cdot 7 \times 10^{-4}$	$0 \cdot 83$	2
Phenol-tetrachloroethane	$(2 \cdot 1 \pm 0 \cdot 3) \times 10^{-4}$	$0 \cdot 82 \pm 0 \cdot 03$	3
Phenol-trichlorophenol	$2 \cdot 1 \times 10^{-4}$	$0 \cdot 80$	4
Phenol-tetrachloroethane	$7 \cdot 55 \times 10^{-4}$	$0 \cdot 685$	5
Phenol-trichlorophenol	$2 \cdot 13 \times 10^{-3}$	$0 \cdot 588$	6
Phenol-tetrachloroethane	$0 \cdot 92 \times 10^{-4}$	$0 \cdot 85$	7

The spread of values represented, even where the same solvent is used, gives some idea of the difficulty of selecting the 'best' equation for the polymer, and in summary it is simplest to say that M_n for commercial polymers having intrinsic viscosities of 0·6–0·7 is most probably somewhere between 16,000 and 30,000. The distribution of molecular weights in poly(ethylene terephthalate) has been studied by various workers,[5,8] who conclude that it is in accordance with the predictions of the Schulz-Flory theory; Haseley[6] has shown that polymer of $[\eta] = 0.62$ contains material of M_n as low as 5,300 and as high as 49,000. An equation due to Flory relates the viscosities (η) of molten aliphatic polyesters to their weight-average molecular weights (M_w) as follows:[9,10]

$$\log \eta = A + BM_w^{\frac{1}{2}}$$

(where A and B are constants at a given temperature).

It is not known whether molten poly(ethylene terephthalate) conforms to this expression, but as a practical guide it can be stated that the melt viscosities of the polymer at 280°C lie between 1900 and 3000 poises for intrinsic viscosities of 0·6–0·7.

Returning to the chemical structure of the polymer, one minor side-reaction of polycondensation comprises the etherification of ethylene glycol (or perhaps of di-2-hydroxyethyl terephthalate) to 3-oxapentamethylene glycol ('diethylene glycol') which becomes incorporated in the polymer chain as units of the type

$\sim\!\phi\cdot CO\cdot O\cdot (CH_2)_2\cdot O\cdot (CH_2)_2\cdot O\cdot OC\cdot\phi\!\sim$. Another structural modification is caused by side-reactions of thermal degradation which, perhaps not surprisingly, cannot be entirely eliminated at the high temperatures required for reaction. The course of this reaction at 282°C, which has been elucidated by Goodings,[11] can be summarised in Fig. 3.1.

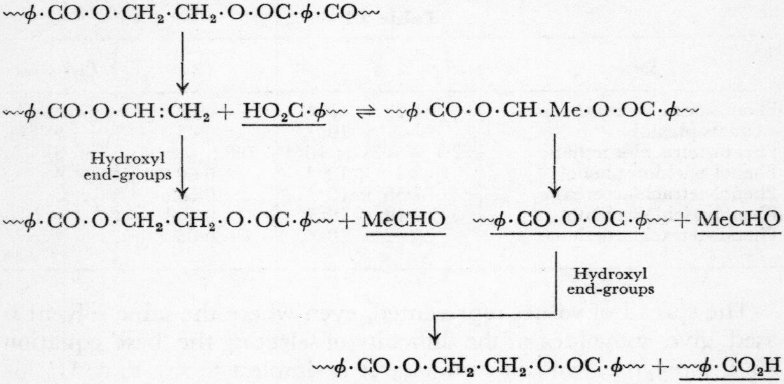

$\sim\!\phi\cdot CO\cdot O\cdot CH_2\cdot CH_2\cdot O\cdot OC\cdot\phi\cdot CO\!\sim$

$\downarrow$

$\sim\!\phi\cdot CO\cdot O\cdot CH:CH_2 + \underline{HO_2C\cdot\phi\!\sim} \rightleftharpoons \sim\!\phi\cdot CO\cdot O\cdot CH\cdot Me\cdot O\cdot OC\cdot\phi\!\sim$

Hydroxyl end-groups

$\sim\!\phi\cdot CO\cdot O\cdot CH_2\cdot CH_2\cdot O\cdot OC\cdot\phi\!\sim + \underline{MeCHO}$ $\sim\!\phi\cdot \underline{CO\cdot O\cdot OC}\cdot\phi\!\sim + \underline{MeCHO}$

Hydroxyl end-groups

$\sim\!\phi\cdot CO\cdot O\cdot CH_2\cdot CH_2\cdot O\cdot OC\cdot\phi\!\sim + \sim\!\underline{\phi\cdot CO_2H}$

Fig. 3.1

Here the species underlined (carboxyl-terminated chains, in-chain anhydride groups, and acetaldehyde) are novel structural entities, not obvious products of polyesterification. Acetaldehyde is indeed evolved in small amounts during polymerisation and can itself undergo further reactions of condensation to semi-polymeric material with the elimination of water, which can attack already-formed ester groups by hydrolysis to produce further carboxyl end-groups. The vinyl terephthalate end-groups formed at an early stage can also undergo further reactions of addition polymerisation,[12] but despite this complex of processes the main result at ordinary processing temperatures is to introduce a certain proportion of carboxyl end-groups into the polymer structure. Of course higher temperatures (above 300°C) can produce more deep-seated changes, yielding a variety of complex aromatic acid units, aromatic ketone groups, styrene-like structures, etc., with the concomitant elimination of carbon monoxide, methane, acetylene, and other gases,[11-14] but the contribution of these changes to structural aberrations in the normal polymer is negligible.

The largest departure from strict linearity of structure in poly(ethylene terephthalate) arises from the presence in it of cyclic ethylene terephthalates. The existence of a solvent-extractable component in the commercial polymer was first recognised by Ross and co-workers,[15] who extracted from Mylar film a small amount of a high-melting compound which was suggested to be tris(ethylene terephthalate) (Fig. 3.2 (a), $n = 2$). A later study[16] confirmed this formula and showed that the compound was accompanied by smaller amounts of the cyclic tetramer and pentamer of ethylene terephthalate (Fig. 3.2 (a); $n = 3$, 4) together with a further cyclic compound (Fig. 3.2 (b)), present to the extent of less than 0·1% in the polymer. This contains the 3-oxapentamethylene residue and is clearly a product of the etherification side-reaction.

$$OC \cdot \phi \cdot CO \cdot O \cdot CH_2 \cdot CH_2 \cdot O$$
$$[O \cdot CH_2 \cdot CH_2 \cdot O \cdot OC \cdot \phi \cdot CO]_n$$

(a)

$$OC \cdot \phi \cdot CO \cdot O \cdot CH_2 \cdot CH_2 \cdot O \cdot OC \cdot \phi \cdot CO$$
$$O - CH_2 \cdot CH_2 \cdot O \cdot CH_2 \cdot CH_2 - O$$

(b)

Fig. 3.2

These cyclic compounds, which together amount to about 1·5–1·7% of the weight of commercial polymer samples, exist in equilibrium with the molten linear polymer and are formed rapidly when all-linear polymer is raised to just above its melting point; they are thus inescapable constituents of all melt-processed fibres and films. In certain circumstances they may migrate or be extracted from such products,[17] but apart from this loss (which is finite since the compounds are not re-formed below 260°C) the polymer is resistant to the majority of common organic solvents at ordinary temperatures.

Various organic liquids dissolve poly(ethylene terephthalate) at elevated temperatures; they include dimethyl sulphone, biphenyl, diphenyl oxide, ethers of the anisole type, aromatic ketones, dibutyl phthalate, substituted phosphoramides, and some heterocyclic compounds. The polymer is not dissolved appreciably by aliphatic hydrocarbons or mineral oils, even at high temperatures, and the only liquids known to dissolve it at normal temperatures are the fluorinated and chlorinated acetic acids, phenols, and anhydrous hydrofluoric acid. Chloroform has the peculiar property of dissolving amorphous poly(ethylene terephthalate) at temperatures below 0°C, but on warming such solutions the polymer separates in crystalline form and chloroform is without effect on polymer which has already been crystallised.

A fundamental characteristic of poly(ethylene terephthalate) is its ability to be quenched from the melt to an amorphous form which persists indefinitely at room temperature. The amorphous substance is a clear brittle resin, isotropic to normal examination although Kargin[18] believes that it possesses some degree of pre-crystalline order. Thermal crystallisation in spherulitic forms takes place when the amorphous polymer is heated without the application of an orienting stress to 100°C or higher—that is, to temperatures higher than the glass/rubber transition range—or when the molten polymer is slowly cooled to 230–240°C. The importance of crystallisation in fabrication processes for the polymer has led to detailed studies of this transformation from the morphological and kinetic points of view.[19-24] The rate of crystallisation increases with temperature from 100°C up to 180–190°C, where it is at a maximum, and the character of crystallisation at various temperatures depends on the previous thermal history of the material and on the temperature to which it has been raised in the molten state. These factors control the occurrence and number of crystal nuclei and determine whether the crystallisation of a sample of the polymer occurs by the steady growth of spherulites around nuclei already present, or from centres appearing sporadically at different times giving a range of numbers and sizes of spherulites. The rate of crystallisation is also sensitive to the molecular weight of the material, being slower for the more highly polymeric samples, and the optical character of the spherulites (which reflects the molecular geometry of crystal growth) can be altered by changes in the drying history of the polymer. The rate of crystallisation of films of amorphous poly(ethylene terephthalate) of intrinsic viscosity 0·50, quenched after fusion at 280°C, varies with temperature according to the following equation which is due to Golike and Cobbs:[25]

$$\log \frac{1}{t_{\frac{1}{2}}} = 1\cdot97 - \frac{137}{T - T_g} - 1\cdot03 \left[\frac{1}{T} \left(\frac{T_m}{T_m - T} \right)^2 \right]$$

Here $t_{\frac{1}{2}}$ is the half-time of crystallisation in minutes at $T°C$, and T_m, T_g are the melting and glass-rubber transition temperatures (°C), respectively. Following the initial rapid crystallisation which is accompanied by a quick and marked increase in the density of the material, a slow, small increase in density can be observed;[22,26]

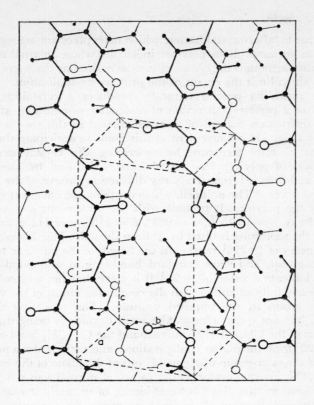

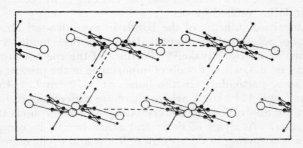

Fig. 3.3   Arrangement of molecules in the crystal of poly(ethylene terephthalate).   Top: Projection normal to (010) plane.   Bottom: Projection along C axis.   (Larger dot—carbon; smaller dot—hydrogen; open circles—oxygen)

this is due to 'after-crystallisation' which takes place among segments of the as yet amorphous polymer molecules whose thermal motion gradually surmounts the obstacles such as molecular chain-entanglements which limit the extent of the primary crystallisation.

The annealing process naturally produces a crystalline mass devoid of a preferred direction of molecular orientation, and the X-ray diffraction pattern of material treated in this way is of the powder type. It is convenient at this point to anticipate the later account of fibre structure by describing the crystal structure (Fig. 3.3) of poly(ethylene terephthalate) deduced by Daubeny, Bunn, and Brown[27] from the X-ray diffraction pattern of the highly oriented fibres. The unit cell, which contains one chemical repeat-unit of the polymer, is triclinic with the dimensions $a = 4 \cdot 56$ Å, $b = 5 \cdot 94$ Å, $c = 10 \cdot 75$ Å, $\alpha = 98\frac{1}{2}°$, $\beta = 118°$, $\gamma = 112°$; the long axis of the molecules is tilted by $5°$ from the axis of the fibres. The c dimension of $10 \cdot 75$ Å represents the length of the ethylene terephthalate group, and since standard bond-lengths and bond-angles would indicate a value of $10 \cdot 9$ Å it is clear that the molecules are very nearly fully extended with the combining atoms of the terephthalate group in the opposed position. The repeating unit is nearly, but not quite, planar, the small deviations being due to a rotation of the CH_2—CH_2 bonds around the O—CH_2 bond-axis by about $20°$ from the planar configuration; and there is also a possible twist of the ester-group of about $12°$ out of the plane of the benzene ring. The intermolecular distances are of normal van der Waals dimensions, so that there is no evidence of specially strong forces between neighbouring chains such as occur, for example, in the hydrogen-bonded polyamides, and the packing of molecular chains leaves no large unfilled spaces.

Structural assignments of the bands in the infra-red absorption spectrum of poly(ethylene terephthalate) have been made by Grime and Ward[28] and by Miyake.[29] Portions of the spectra are reproduced in Fig. 3.4, where details of importance in the present context can be seen, particularly in the bands at 1470 cm^{-1}, 1445 cm^{-1}, 1370 cm^{-1} and 1340 cm^{-1}, where there are differences in intensity between the absorptions of the crystalline and amorphous states of the polymer. Analyses of these and other bands, in comparison with bands occurring in the spectra of linear and cyclic oligomers of ethylene terephthalate, have been interpreted in terms of configurational changes in the ethylenedioxy part of the repeat unit, according to which the crystalline portion of the material contains this grouping in the thermodynamically favoured *trans* conformation,

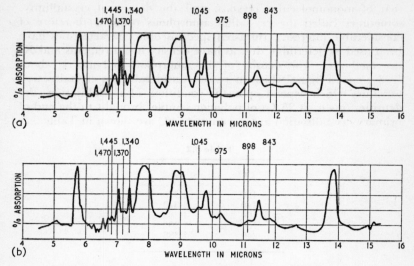

Fig. 3.4 Infra-red absorption spectra of amorphous (A) and crystalline (B) poly(ethylene terephthalate)

(a) *TRANS* CONFIGURATION OF ETHYLENE DIOXY GROUPS IN THE CRYSTALLINE STATE
(b) ADDITIONAL *GAUCHE* CONFIGURATION OCCURRING IN THE AMORPHOUS MATERIAL

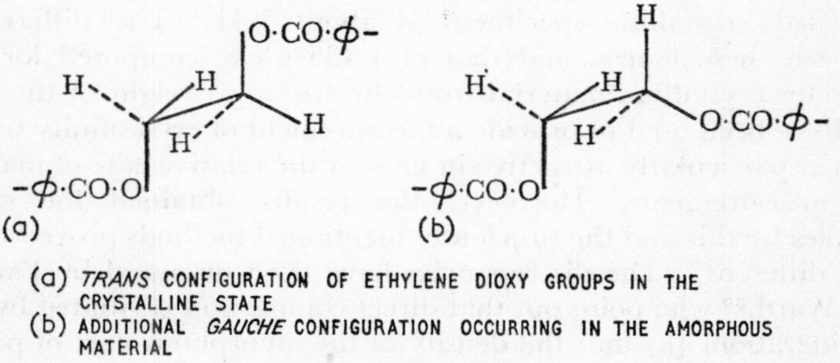

Fig. 3.5 Configurations in poly(ethylene terephthalate)

whilst the amorphous phase also contains the isomeric *gauche* conformation (Fig. 3.5). This implies that the process of ordering of molecules during crystallisation takes place through, or is at least accompanied by, conformational changes in the aliphatic portions of the polymer chains, leading to the configuration of maximum stability.

As with crystalline polymers in general, the crystallinity of poly(ethylene terephthalate) is far from perfect in comparison with that of monomolecular crystals, and the degree of crystallinity, sometimes called the crystalline/amorphous ratio, is therefore of considerable interest.   Infra-red spectroscopic characteristics have been used to determine this, as have density measurements and X-ray methods.   The density of the amorphous polymer is about 1·33 g/c.c., a figure which increases considerably on crystallisation to values which depend upon the conditions of crystallisation; the densities (g/c.c. at 25°C) of polymer samples brought to the end of primary crystallisation at temperatures t°C are shown in Table 3.2.

Table 3.2

t°C	d
120	1·376
140	1·379
160	1·385
180	1·387
240	1·388

Commercial fibres and films of poly(ethylene terephthalate) have densities of 1·38, and the highest value which has been found for annealed crystalline specimens is about 1·41.   The differences between these figures and that of 1·455 g/c.c. computed for the perfectly crystalline material from the size and weight of the unit cell have been used to provide a measurement of crystallinity which seemed particularly attractive in view of the relative ease of making the measurements.   However, the results obtained for given samples by this and the previously mentioned methods proved to be very different.   The discrepancies have been discussed by Farrow and Ward,[30] who point out that direct comparison is vitiated by the considerations (a) that the density of the amorphous part of partly crystalline and possibly oriented samples is not necessarily constant, and (b) that the infra-red method is related basically to molecular orientation rather than to three-dimensional crystalline order, these being very different things.   As an approximate guide it can be indicated that drawn and heat-set fibres have X-ray crystallinities of about 40% when the values from density and infra-red measurements are about 60% and 80% respectively.

The glass-rubber transition temperature (T_g) has so far been mentioned only as the temperature below which thermal crystallisation cannot occur.   For non-crystallising polymers it is generally taken as being the temperature zone in which segmental motion of molecules is first apparent. Its significance for crystalline polyesters will be considered in later sections, and here we shall deal only with the actual value for poly(ethylene terephthalate). The locus of T_g on the temperature scale can be determined by various methods including dilatometry, dynamic, and sonic modulus measurements, dielectric measurements, and differential thermal analysis, and the values obtained differ somewhat from one method to another, depending on the equivalent frequencies of the measurements. From dynamic modulus measurements it has been shown that this polymer has *two* principal transition ranges. The main one is that normally recognised as the glass-rubber transition which occurs at 80°C (at 1 c/s) for the amorphous material, but which rises to 125°C with increasing crystallinity, whilst the second occurs at −40°C and is much less sensitive to crystallinity.[31]

Some further useful data can be summarised simply. The specific heat varies somewhat with the state of the sample[32] but has a value around 0·3 cal/g°C; the coefficient of thermal conductivity is 4×10^{-4} cal cm/sq cm°C sec, and that of thermal expansion $2·7 \times 10^{-4}$ cm/cm°C. Apparent values for the latent heat of fusion have been given as between 9 or 11–16 cal/g[33,34], but Smith and Dole point out the significance of crystallite size in arriving at a proper figure, and conclude that the correct value at 200°C is 30·4 cal/g.[32] The ultra-violet absorption spectrum is substantially the same as those of simple alkyl terephthalates;[35,36] the longest wavelength band has its maximum at 288 mμ, above which absorption falls off rapidly to virtually nil at 370 mμ.[37] The permeability of 100-gauge film to water vapour at 38°C and 90% relative humidity is 21 g/m²/day, whilst film of the same gauge permits the passage of 2,900, 109, and 43 cc of hydrogen, oxygen, and nitrogen, respectively, through 1 m² in 24 hours under 1 atmosphere partial pressure gradient. The solubilities and diffusion of other gases in poly(ethylene terephthalate) samples of different physical states have been studied;[38,39] the molecular sizes and dipole moments of the gases govern the relative rates of permeation, and in most cases there is a discontinuity of the variation of solubility and diffusion constants with temperature at about the T_g.

3.3 THE FORMATION, STRUCTURE, AND PROPERTIES OF FIBRES

The principal molecular characteristic of the fibrous state consists in the presence of a substantial degree of polymer chain orientation directed along the length of the filaments. In the practical polyester fibres this is associated also with the presence of a degree of oriented crystallinity, and this structural combination has to be imposed upon a starting material—the bulk-polymer resulting from polymerisation—which is itself devoid of molecular order. Rather similar requirements apply to the formation of polyester films, and although the technologies of film and fibre manufacture are necessarily distinct, they have a good deal in common at the fundamental level.

3.3.1   SPINNING AND DRAWING OF FIBRES

Of the various means for the conversion of polymers to fibres, one only (melt-spinning) is of present-day importance for polyester fibre manufacture. This conversion requires two stages—spinning and drawing—and it is normal for the drawn fibres to be stabilised by heat-setting at some time before reaching the final user. For staple-type yarns this stabilisation is carried out by the fibre manufacturer, whilst for other types the operation may not take place until considerably later in the chain of textile operations, when the material is already in fabric or other woven form; but, as will be seen, the details of the three processes jointly determine the physical properties of the resultant fibres.

In the spinning operation, the 'chip' or flake form of the polyester is melted, with protection against the degradative effects of moisture or oxygen at the necessary high temperatures, and the molten polymer is filtered and then pumped through the fine holes of a spinneret plate into air at normal temperature. The consequent rapid heat loss causes quenching of the filaments so obtained, and these are collected as the so-called 'spun-yarn', a weak, extensible, and amorphous material. The filaments at this stage are usually moistened with a textile spin-finish which serves to lubricate them, to dispel static charge, and to cause bundles of fibres temporarily to cohere so that they can be controlled throughout the remainder of the process.

In the second part of the process, the drawing stage, the strands of spun yarn are stretched whilst being heated to above the glass-transition temperature whereby molecular orientation and crystallinity are induced. In its simplest form continuous drawing is accomplished by passing the yarn through a device consisting of two revolving rollers, the more distant rotating faster than the first so that the moving filaments are extended under tension; but in practice the machines are complex in construction, having pins, tension gates, and heaters of various types inserted in the path of the moving filaments to improve and control their running. Marshall and Thompson describe the physical basis of these operations in some detail.[40-42] Following drawing, yarns intended for staple fibre uses are normally crimped and heat-set before being cut up to the desired lengths and baled; those destined for use in continuous-filament form are wound on to bobbins and sold thus for the further purposes of textile manufacture.

An outline of the properties of commercial polyester fibres has already been given in Section 1.3, and for full practical details of

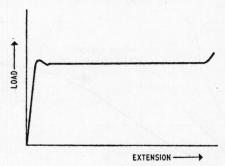

*Fig. 3.6   Form of load/extension curve for spun
polyester yarns (schematic)*

their use and behaviour reference should be made to the excellent technical publications of the manufacturers. Here we shall deal more closely with the connection between the properties in general and the molecular constitution of the fibres.

Polyester spun-yarns, like those of many other crystalline and some non-crystalline polymers, possess the property of cold-drawing; that is, on being stretched, they do not extend by continuous flow in the way shown by a rubber band, but instead narrow down at some points to 'necks' of smaller diameter than the filament, and the length increases by the moving apart of the 'necking' points as the stretching force is maintained. The load/extension characteristics of this behaviour are indicated schematically in Fig. 3.6 which shows that, following the initial yield, such filaments increase in length to constant tension up to a point when they suddenly toughen and, if the tension is increased, break. The tension of drawing is largely concentrated in the 'necks', and it is here where the orientation of molecules occurs. The maximum draw-ratio of poly(ethylene terephthalate) filaments is about 6 : 1 (i.e. the filaments can be extended by stretching by about 600%), though the draw-ratios used in making practical fibres are in the more restricted range of 3–5 : 1, the actual value used depending on the yarn type being made.

As indicated previously, Terylene fibres are manufactured in three main types—as staple fibre, and as filament yarns of medium and

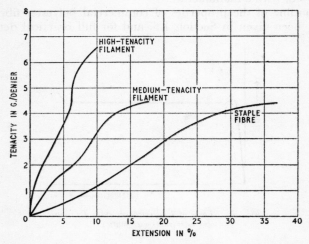

Fig. 3.7   Load/extension curves for different types of Terylene fibres

high tenacity, which have different characteristics of tensile behaviour (see Table 1.1 and Fig. 3.7) and hence of application. These differences reflect differences of fine molecular structure, primarily of orientation. The amount of orientation in drawn samples of fibres and films depends on the rate and temperature at which stretching is done, on the extent (or ratio) of stretch, on the molecular weight of the polymer, and on the thermal and processing history of the samples; it can therefore be varied over a considerable range.[43]   Staple-type fibres are made by spinning at relatively low speeds and drawing to a limited extent, whilst the continuous-filament types are obtained by spinning at higher speeds followed by drawing to medium or high draw-ratios, for the medium- and high-tenacity types, respectively.   The duration of the drawing process is too short for the fibres to undergo a thorough molecular equilibration, and the internal strains in the as-drawn yarns are manifest by their shrinkage on heating (which amounts to about 7% in boiling water or 10–16% in air above 140°C). In the heat-setting or stabilisation process they are heated for periods sufficient to release the strain and to promote crystallisation to the fullest possible extent. Setting may be carried out in the temperature range 120°C to 220°C, with the fibre or fabric held at constant dimensions, or with controlled shrinkage, or with completely free relaxation, and since these alternatives obviously have different effects on the fine internal structure, they can be used in conjunction with the varied drawing processes to give any desired pattern of tensile properties that is consistent with the ultimate capabilities of the material. Thus one can seek to match the detailed mechanical properties of wool, rayon, cotton, sisal, etc., which may have to be blended with the polyester for textile use. Heat-setting reduces the shrinkage of polyester fibres to 1–2% at 150°C and renders them dimensionally stable to temperatures up to that at which stabilisation was effected.

Any one polyester sample can thus be converted to a range of fibrous products having different internal structures and corres-

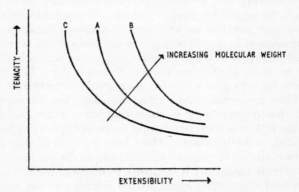

Fig. 3.8   Ultimate properties curves for polyester yarns of different molecular weights (schematic)

pondingly different mechanical properties. Such properties can be summarised as an 'ultimate properties' curve of the type shown as A in Fig. 3.8, constructed from the tenacities and extensibilities to break of the various fibre types which can be derived from the polymer. A polyester sample of higher molecular weight will give a slightly different curve (B), whereas a lower molecular weight will yield another curve (C) for the various derivable products. Moderate changes in molecular weight thus provide a further means to alter the combinations of properties in polyester fibres, as has been suggested for the control of pilling in fabrics.[44]

3.3.2   CRYSTALLINITY OF FIBRES

We have now to consider the structure of the fibres themselves, and since the following discussion must inevitably bear on crystallinity it is as well to remember that the picture of spherulitic crystallisation given in Section 3.2 concerns only thermal crystallisation of the polymer in bulk and that it is not directly relevant to fibres whose crystallinity, induced by drawing, is in non-spherulitic forms.

The optical-microscopic examination of polyester fibres does not disclose any gross morphological internal features such as are found in wool or cotton.   It is doubtful whether they have any distinctive structure apparent to the electron-microscope, although some claims have been made to have detected fibrillar entities at this level.   It is certain however, that polyester fibres are not structurally homogeneous at the molecular level.   The early 'fringed micelle' theory of fibre structure asserted the existence of discrete crystalline parts in fibres, immersed in and separated by an amorphous magma, with chain molecules most likely passing through several crystalline and amorphous zones at different parts of their lengths.   This appeared for a long time to give a reasonable qualitative model in terms of which fibre properties could be understood, but in recent years evidence has accumulated to show that the picture could not be reconciled in detail with newer and more precise crystallographic, mechanical, and other data.   The whole question of fibre structure is therefore subject to enquiry and revision at the present time, and in its currently fluid state it is unwise to do more here than outline the principal contending ideas, with a warning to the reader that some of these are highly controversial, that not all necessarily apply to polyester fibres, and that a modern commonly accepted view is still to be formulated.

Completely opposed to the 'fringed micelle' theory is the view championed by certain Russian scientists, notably Kargin[18] and Mikhailov,[45] that fibres are not crystalline at all in the classical sense but that what is called 'crystallinity' is simply a state of molecular order which is at a low (but still real) level in so-called amorphous polymers, and greater in the so-called crystalline ones. Stuart, on the other hand, suggests that there is a crystalline lattice (in the classical sense) which is essentially continuous throughout the fibre but which has intermittent regions of defects or lesser order.[46]   A somewhat related view, given by Hosemann,[47] pictures fibres as composed of, or at least containing, 'paracrystals' which are lattice-like aggregates of chain molecules devoid of long-range order but which possess finite order over limited molecular distances; that is, successive chain-segments are located with reference only to their nearest neighbours, not to more distant units in the same or nearby chains.   Another view of fibre structure, so far adumbrated only for the polyamides but which may also have relevance elsewhere, uses the hypothesis of folded molecules recently put forward to explain the structures of single crystals of high polymers and postulates the presence of crystalline aggregates or lamellae having constant lengths of about 80 Å in the direction of the fibre axis, composed of chain molecules mostly folded at the lamellar surfaces but with some chains running directly without folding into the structures of the aggregates stacked above and below, thus providing a structural continuity along the fibre.[48]   These latter views discount, in effect, the old purely amorphous phase; but this does figure in another view[49] which modifies the 'fringed micelle' picture to one of 'fringed fibrils' where long strands or ropes of molecules stretch along the fibre and are separated laterally by randomly disposed amorphous chains.

Some part, at least, of the difficulty in describing fibre structure stems from difficulties in defining what is meant by crystallinity. Conventionally this is taken to refer to a precise location of identical units in a three-dimensional domain of sufficient extent to produce characteristic responses under optical, X-ray, or thermal examination, and, as implied above, some investigators are now prepared to accept that such domains may contain defects of substantial extent. Around such domains, or around segment bundles, there are likely to be unfilled spaces or voids which, it is claimed, can be studied qualitatively by small-angle X-ray scattering techniques.[50]   The question of definition is also made more complicated by the recognition[51] that all of the apparent characteristics of crystallinity may be present in bulk or fibre samples of polyesters whose chemical structures are inherently incapable of full three-dimensional order; this subject will be resumed in Section 4.3.

Returning now to fibres of poly(ethylene terephthalate), we know from what was said earlier concerning the actual crystal structure that molecules in the crystalline state are directed along the fibre axis and are in the virtually fully extended close-packed configuration. We know that there is also a proportion of molecules, or segments of molecules, having a *gauche* configuration of the ethylene-dioxy groups which, on shape grounds alone, cannot occupy normal lattice positions; we know also that the amounts of crystallinity and of orientation, however defined or measured, can be varied by changing the conditions of the fibre-making processes. It is inferred, moreover, from the dynamic mechanical behaviour of such fibres, and confirmed by nuclear magnetic resonance studies, that segmental motion of molecules occurs over a wide range of temperatures, and that the capacity for molecular rotations or other movements must therefore be present in the structure. In view of the uncertain contemporary picture of fibre structure it is inappropriate to discuss here how these facts conform with the individual possibilities mentioned above, and as a practical summary we shall conclude with the view that Terylene fibres behave as if they contained two conterminous types of structural organisation, crystalline and amorphous, each in varying degrees of perfection and with a range of degrees of orientation in both types. The relative proportions of crystalline and amorphous substance depend largely, though not entirely, on the thermal history, whereas the degree of orientation depends mainly on the drawing history. If the crystalline material is considered to exist in discrete crystallites of the type envisaged in the 'fringed micelle' theory, then crystallographic data would suggest that they have sizes of 50–80 Å both along and transverse to the fibre axis;[52] but the derivation of this result depends on a structural assumption which may not be true.

On heating normal stabilised Terylene fibres between room temperature and the melting point, no significant change in the crystalline characteristics is noted till about 235°C, when the crystal structure undergoes disorientation, though the unoriented material does not melt till the usual temperature of just over 260°C.[53] Meanwhile, certain other properties attributable to the behaviour of the amorphous zones have undergone more definite changes. The tenacity falls slowly and progressively (though recoverably on cooling) to a value which, at 200°C, is only 40% of that at 20°C, and the extensibility correspondingly increases. These effects are extended in the same sense at the other end of the temperature scale so that, relative to 20°C, the tenacity is increased at −100°C by 50% and the extensibility reduced by 35%. Another important change is the fall in modulus which occurs above 100°C, in the region of the glass-transition temperature;[31] it is due to this change that the permanent pleating of Terylene is possible by pressing the fabrics at temperatures of 120–150°C, and the facts that the glass transition occurs in this region and that it is not depressed significantly when the fibres are wetted (as happens with more hydrophilic fibres) explains why the same material resists wrinkling in ordinary conditions of wear. Molecular motion in poly(ethylene terephthalate) and in its homologues has been studied over a wide range of

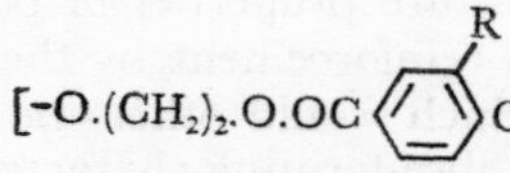

$$[-O.(CH_2)_2.O.OC \langle \underset{R}{\bigcirc} \rangle CO-]_n$$

R = Me *or* OMe

Fig. 3.9

temperatures by Ward and co-workers[54–56] and by Hyndman and Origlio,[57] and the results provide interesting independent confirmation of the state of the amorphous component inferred by other techniques. Briefly, at temperatures from −180°C to the glass-transition temperature, only slight molecular motion occurs, mostly hindered rotation of the methylene groups. Above 110°C, other motions, including rotations of the benzene rings around the phenylene-carbonyl axis, can be detected and, as the temperature is raised, eventually most of the molecular material in the non-crystalline part of the polymer becomes involved in local motion. Whilst the results of nuclear magnetic resonance studies agree with the X-ray indications that the aromatic rings of the crystalline domains are rigid above the glass-transition temperature, they suggest that some measure of hindered rotation may also be occurring in the aliphatic portions of the crystalline zones at high temperatures.

The interpretation of physical properties in poly(ethylene terephthalate) given above and in Section 3.2 thus places great weight on the behaviour of the amorphous component. The relative contributions of this and of the crystalline component can be inferred from studies on the analogous polymers, poly(ethylene methylterephthalate) or poly(ethylene methoxyterephthalate) (Fig. 3.9).[58] When these are prepared by normal high-temperature polycondensation, the random order of presentation of reactant molecules, together with the ester-metathesis reactions which occur at high temperatures,[59] will assure that the placement of R groups in successive chain-units of the polymer has a statistical distribution over all possible positions. The resultant structure is therefore geometrically irregular and the polymers do not crystallise. Their skeletons resemble that of Terylene and the compounds can be converted to drawn fibres having reasonable tensile properties. However, on warming to their glass-transition temperatures (about 100°C) they show the typical behaviour of amorphous thermoplastic polymers in softening and being attenuated on stretching to syrupy threadlike forms, devoid of strength. This behaviour suggests that the superior high-temperature properties of poly(ethylene terephthalate) fibres are due to reinforcement by the crystalline material against larger changes which would otherwise occur in the amorphous zones, but that the fibre-forming character is a property of the *whole* substance in orientation rather than of the crystalline component alone.

3.3.3   RESPONSE OF FIBRES TO CHEMICAL REAGENTS AND RADIATION

Any description of polyester fibres must contain some account of their response towards the effects of chemicals and radiation, both obviously important matters in the textile context, and since this behaviour is more dependent on the chemical constitution than on microphysical structure (though this is not entirely without influence), the facts will also be relevant to the performance of the polymers in film form.

The characteristic chemical reactions to be expected of linear polyesters—hydrolysis, alcoholysis, aminolysis, etc.—are all likely to produce chain breakages and hence, through reduction of molecular weight, a deterioration of physical properties. The susceptibilities of different classes of polyesters to attack by these agencies can vary greatly with structure, depending on whether the hydroxylic precursors are of the aliphatic or phenolic hydroxyl type, or, in the case of the acids, whether these are aliphatic or aromatic. Polyesters derived from aliphatic acids or from phenolic substances tend to be most labile and sensitive to chemical attack whereas the aromatic acid-aliphatic diol type, exemplified in Terylene and Kodel, is the most stable; the differences in reactivity over the whole range of polyester types amounts to several orders of magnitude (see also Section 4.6).

Practical polyester fibres and films show excellent resistance to attack by water, dilute mineral acids, and common aqueous oxidising agents; they are also substantially inert to the common organic solvents in ordinary conditions. They are more sensitive to these agents at higher temperatures, however, and to the action of alkalis, ammoniacal solutions, and organic bases, even at room temperature. A comprehensive study of the hydrolysis and atmospheric oxidation of poly(ethylene terephthalate) films and fibres over a wide range of temperatures and humidities concludes that, at 100°C and 100% relative humidity, hydrolysis exceeds oxidation by a rate-factor of 5,000, so that the latter is of negligible extent, and that at moderate temperatures and humidities the life of the materials would amount to many years.[60] In practical terms, fibres can be retained almost indefinitely in water at 70°C without detrimental effect but, at 100°C, 60% of the tenacity is lost after three weeks; at higher temperatures the rate of attack by water or by moist air is proportionately increased by 1·082 times per °C rise in temperature. The effects of elevated temperatures in normal atmospheres are probably wholly due to hydrolysis by the small amount of moisture present in the air and, as a guide, it can be said that, after six weeks at 150°C, Terylene fibres lose 20–25% of their original tenacities, and only 50% after 28 weeks; this behaviour compares extremely well with that shown by most other filamentary materials. Kinetic studies on the hydrolysis of the polymer by water at various elevated temperatures indicate that the reaction is not diffusion-controlled.[61]

The action of aqueous hydrochloric acid solutions depends on the acid concentration and temperature; acid of 30% strength has no effect on the tenacity at 40°C in 48 hours, though at 80°C the same acid reduces fibre tenacity by 70% in the same time. Sulphuric acid of 10% strength has little more effect than water alone; even 50% acid requires six months at 50°C to halve the tenacity of fibres, although this attack is considerably speeded by heating to 70°C. Sulphuric acid of concentrations greater than 83%, however, no longer attacks polyester fibres by slow hydrolysis but dissolves them completely with total degradation. Attack by nitric acid of moderate strengths is also limited in extent at ordinary temperatures, but it is greatly accelerated by warming; weaker, non-oxidising, and organic acids (except those halogenated acids which dissolve the polymer) have very little effect on polyesters.

Basic substances react with polyesters differently according to whether they are ionic or not. The former (substances such as caustic soda, lime water, sodium silicate, etc.) do not penetrate the structure but affect the outer surface of the filaments or films; organic bases and ammonia, on the other hand, diffuse into the material and attack it in depth. Thus, whereas sodium hydroxide solutions dissolve away the surface of the polymer, leaving the undissolved part unimpaired (except for dimensions), ammonia or amines break the polymer molecules by amide-formation with consequent weakening whose extent is in proportion to the temperature and severity of treatment; a 15% solution of ammonia at 20°C reduces the strength of Terylene fibres by 5% in 24 hours and by 30% in 10 days, whereas a 1% solution at 100°C reduces the strength by half in 10 hours. Structural investigations of the course of degradation by methylamine suggest that, as with attack by hydrochloric acid, degradation proceeds first and most rapidly in the unoriented amorphous phase, and then with increasing difficulty in the unoriented crystalline and oriented crystalline materials.[62] Microscopic examination of the surfaces of polyester films etched by treatment with propylamine at room temperature reveals lines, lamellae, or brick-like structures of micron size whose form and frequency depends on the history of processing and orientation.[63]

The resistance of poly(ethylene terephthalate) to photochemical degradation or weathering is extremely good, being exceeded among other common polymers which have not been specially stabilised only by polyacrylonitrile. Such long-term degradation as does occur appears to be initiated by light of ultraviolet wavelengths[37] which is filtered from daylight by passage through glass. Samples exposed behind windowglass thus have a very good life indeed. Mechanistic understanding of the reactions occurring during the photodegradation of polyesters is very rudimentary although suggestions have been made of breakdown by a free-radical decomposition process.[64] It is also a matter of observation that poly(ethylene terephthalate) is one of the most resistant of polymers to degradation by nuclear radiations. The effects vary with the orientation of the sample, the nature and duration of the radiation, and the presence or absence of oxygen, but they are generally to reduce the physical properties. Again the mechanistic details are unknown, but some authors postulate that cross-linking can occur.[65-67]

3.3.4 PIGMENTATION AND DYEING OF FIBRES

For textile purposes it is obviously necessary to be able to colour polyester fibres, which may be done either by the incorporation of pigments into the polymers prior to spinning or by dyeing in fibre or fabric form. On account of the complex colour demands of the clothing industry, dyeing (which places great flexibility in the hands of the textile finisher) is incomparably the more important of the two approaches, and whilst the detailed technology and art of the process is beyond the scope of this Monograph, a little must be said about the principles of procedure.

Many of the important processes for dyeing goods made of cotton, wool, silk, or the nylons depend upon the penetration of the fibres by dye molecules which are ionic in character and which then undergo

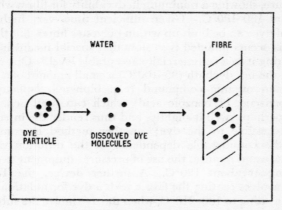

Fig. 3.10   Dispersed dyeing of polyester fibres

combination with the fibre molecules by direct bonding or by hydrogen-bonding. Such dyestuffs generally do not penetrate into polyesters which, furthermore, lack the typical dye-receptor sites present in the other fibres. The dyeing of polyester fibres is therefore based upon a different molecular principle, similar to that used with cellulose acetate rayons, which takes advantage of the physico-chemical partition of a special class of dyes between the polyester and an external medium. The dyes in question are non-ionic organic compounds which dissolve in the polyester medium but are only very slightly soluble in water. They are employed as dispersions in water (on which account they are termed 'disperse colours'), and when the fibre is immersed in such dispersions the small amount of dye actually dissolved in the water is extracted from this into the fibre which thus becomes coloured as suggested in Fig. 3.10. The consequent depletion of the aqueous solution causes further dye molecules to pass from the dispersed particles into solution and thence into the fibre, and so the process is sustained.

Dyeing thus depends on the ability of the dyestuff to diffuse into the fibre, and is strongly dependent upon the internal condition of the latter. Briefly, the capacity of fibres to absorb dye is a property of the amorphous regions, and the more highly oriented or the more crystalline the fibres, the less readily does this take place. In fact, the effect of heat-setting is considerably to reduce the rate of dye-uptake, and a graph of the relationship between this rate and the setting temperature closely resembles that of crystallisation rate with temperature, showing a minimum in dyeability for fibres which have been set at 160–180°C. Given sufficient time, very high concentrations of dye can be built up within polyester fibres, but the rate at which this occurs unaided is so slow that special means have to be used to bring it to a commercially acceptable level. One of these is to add to the hot dyebath (95–100°C) a small amount of a so-called 'carrier', an organic compound (e.g. biphenyl, *o*-phenylphenol, dichlorobenzene, or benzoic acid) which can itself penetrate the fibre, or perhaps swell it slightly, and thus render the interior more readily accessible to the dye; another method in common use exploits the considerable dependence of the diffusion rate upon temperature and requires the use of pressure equipment to carry out the dyeing at about 120°C. A further device, the Thermosol process, involves coating the fabric with a dye formulation followed by rapid heating to 180–210°C, when the dye molecules sublime into the fibres, whilst the Vapocol process employs hot trichloroethylene vapours to carry a coating of dye to the fibre interior.

The disperse technique can also be modified to dye polyesters by the azoic principle, where the reactants are allowed to diffuse into the fibre which is then after-treated with nitrous acid to effect colour formation, and in general it is possible to convert polyester fibres to any desired colour or shade with excellent properties of fastness. Whilst there is thus now no technical problem in achieving these results, many investigators are still seeking means to simplify or cheapen the processes, either by chemical modifications to the polymer structure (as will be mentioned later in connection with copolyesters) or by alterations to the physical structure which aim to make it more accessible for diffusion.

Although the foregoing account of fibre production and properties has been primarily concerned with fibres of poly(ethylene terephthalate), most of what has been written applies in principle to other polyesters, including Kodel whose behaviour follows generally similar lines. Since its properties vary in some points of detail, however, a further note on this material is called for. As noted in Section 1.3, the structure of this material (Fig. 1.4 (b)) resembles that of Terylene except that a 1,4-cyclohexylene ring is present in each repeat-unit between the CH_2 groups of the ethylenedioxy unit. These alicyclic rings are mostly in the *trans* form, and the configuration of molecules in the crystalline structure is again linear and almost fully extended.[68] The glass-transition temperature (about 130°C), melting point (about 290°C) and temperature of maximum crystallisation rate (265°C) are all somewhat higher than for Terylene but the normal density (1·22 g/c.c.) is lower. Kodel fibres can be heat-set, if required, to improve their dimensional stability, and typical values for shrinkage are 1% in boiling water or 3% in air at 220°C. Alterations to the processing conditions can again produce fibres having different stress/strain relationships, although, so far as is presently known, the higher tenacities are not attainable with this material, on which account it is not yet being offered for industrial uses. Nevertheless, it is claimed that the properties of the fibre in staple form are quite adequate to meet all reasonable requirements of use in 'wash-and-wear' fabrics for apparel use.[69]

3.4 THE FORMATION AND PROPERTIES OF FILMS

The manufacture of films from poly(ethylene terephthalate) raises molecular problems, due to the amorphous/crystalline properties, similar to those encountered in spinning to fibres, and the stages of film preparation therefore have much in common with those already described. The process begins with melting of the dried polymer and its extrusion through slit dies to give continuous sheets of the required thicknesses which are then cooled rapidly. The film so obtained (which corresponds to 'spun yarn') is amorphous, non-oriented, and unstable to heating above the glass-transition temperature, which causes it to crystallise to the brittle opaque condition. Whilst the quenched film can be used for vacuum- or pressure-forming, when the conditions of drawing and temperature must be carefully controlled to avoid premature crystallisation, the major part of polyester film manufacture continues with orientation and stabilisation stages which resemble those used in fibre-making.

In the first of these, the amorphous film is heated to above 80°C and drawn biaxially (i.e. in two directions at right angles), when the mechanical properties improve and the relative brittleness of the quenched film is lost. The product of this stage is still subject to shrinkage if heated above the drawing temperature and, except where special use is made of this property in encapsulation or for special heat-shrunk packaging purposes, the manufacture is normally completed by heating the film at 200°C with restraint from shrinkage, when crystallisation occurs and the material is rendered dimensionally stable up to the crystallisation temperature.

To obtain film of balanced properties the extents of drawing in the machine and transverse directions are arranged to be equal; but this is open to variation for special products such as the so-called 'tensilised' films, which are stretched more strongly in one direction than the other, giving different strengths in the two directions. The practical arrangements in the sequence of events and the precise control of straining rates and temperatures are of critical importance for the successful drawing of polyester films. According to Scarlett,[70] who describes a form of stentering machine for the purpose, the longitudinal and transverse drawings are applied consecutively and to the extent of 250–350% of the original dimensions (the film thickness is, of course, correspondingly reduced). The first drawing is carried out at temperatures of 80–90°C, where the properties of the amorphous polymer are changing most rapidly and where the work required to stretch the film is at a minimum. The orientation thus imposed alters the properties, however, and a somewhat higher temperature is required in the second (transverse drawing) stage in order to keep the work requirement low and to avoid film breakage. Scarlett's patent contains much informative matter on the influence of drawing conditions upon film properties and can usefully be consulted by the reader who requires more detail than can be given here; the papers of Visser[71] also supplement the information on this subject.

The molecular structure of poly(ethylene terephthalate) films of the quenched and uniaxially and biaxially stretched types has been the subject of extensive study on the part of many workers who have sought to define the processing details in terms of polymer chain configuration and orientation.[72-82] The detailed microstructure of films is no better understood than that of fibres, and from our present standpoint it need only be mentioned that in drawn films the crystallographic (100) planes of the molecules (i.e. the planes in which the benzene rings lie) are parallel to the film surface and normal to the direction of drawing. Whereas uniaxially stretched films have the crystalline chains oriented in one direction only, the direction of stretch, though without even packing in the directions perpendicular to this, two-way stretched films have their molecular chains running in all directions in the film surface, although with the benzene rings still parallel to the surface.

An outline of the uses of poly(ethylene terephthalate) films was presented in Section 1.3, and many other aspects of their behaviour can be inferred from the discussions of molecular and chemical properties already given.   The tensile properties of such films are illustrated in Fig. 3.11 and although they do not fall in the class of low-loss dielectrics, their retention of high mechanical strength over a wide range of temperatures and their insensitivity to moisture makes for special attractiveness in numerous electrical applications

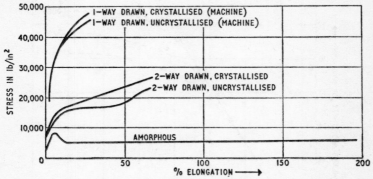

Fig. 3.11   Tensile properties of poly(ethylene terephthalate) films as a function of processing

where the sizes of components can be reduced considerably from those required with traditional insulators.   Reddish has studied the electrical properties of poly(ethylene terephthalate) in detail[83],[84] and some of his data for the volume resistivity, dielectric constant, and power factor of Melinex film in various conditions of temperature and frequency are given in Figs. 3.12, 3.13, and 3.14.

Some properties such as breakdown voltage and shrinkage on heating vary with the film gauge, and the dielectric strength also depends to a considerable degree in practice on the method of construction of components.   Polyester films are still relatively new materials; hence, techniques for ancillary treatments such as resin impregnation, adhesion, and lamination are constantly improving, and recommendations for the best practice of such processes as well as of general handling, printing, and heat-sealing methods, are best sought from the film manufacturers at the time of use.

The advent of poly(cyclohexane-1,4-dimethylene terephthalate) (Fig. 1.4 (b)) as a synthetic material for films is of too recent date for a balanced assessment based on practical experience to be available, but laboratory studies[85] suggest that whilst its processing and

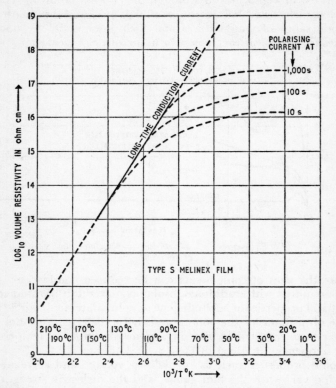

Fig. 3.12   Variation of volume resistivity of Type S Melinex film with temperature

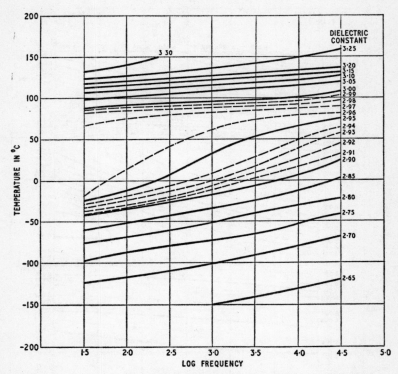

Fig. 3.13   Variation of dielectric constant of Type S Melinex film with temperature and frequency

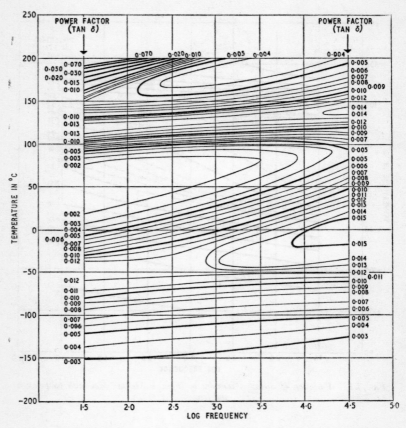

Fig. 3.14   Variation of power factor of Type S Melinex film with temperature and frequency

properties approximately resemble those of poly(ethylene terephthalate), there are some differences of note.   The lower density of the newer polymer permits the production of more film of a given gauge per unit weight of material, but so far as mechanical properties are concerned, the attainable tensile, burst, and tear strengths as well as the modulus and extensibility are all lower than for poly-(ethylene terephthalate).   The somewhat higher glass-transition temperature of Fig. 1.4 (b) ought to imply a better retention of properties at high temperatures, and whilst this appears to be reflected in the dielectric constant and dissipation factor which are more stable above 100°C than for poly(ethylene terephthalate), the poorer resistance of the substance to thermal oxidation and its rapid loss of strength and modulus above 120°C might mitigate these qualities in practice.   On the other hand, the resistance of the newer material towards hydrolysis in moist warm atmospheres is claimed to be better than that of poly(ethylene terephthalate), and the balance of utility between the two clearly depends upon the environmental conditions to be faced.

3.5   GENERAL REMARKS ON FIBRE- AND FILM-FORMING POLYESTERS

The position occupied by poly(ethylene terephthalate) amongst other fibre- and film-forming polymers is due less to any singly identifiable quality than to the possession of properties which, in combination, make for exceptional versatility as indicated by the range of uses.

Poly(ethylene terephthalate) stands together with the nylons and polypropylene in the group of fibrous materials of exceptional strength.   Each has its special characteristics of tensile and extension behaviour, modulus, abrasion resistance, resilience, and handle which designate it for some special area of textile use.   For example, the greater elasticity of the nylons makes them particularly suitable for stockings; the thermal properties of the polyester and its capacity to take pleats which survive repeated washing direct it distinctively towards the woven outerwear section of the clothing trade; the great strength and low cost of polypropylene fibres offer special promise in fishing-net and rope construction.   Each fibre, on the other hand, has some weakness or limitation which excludes it from certain areas.   The nylons are the more sensitive to attack by acids and to oxidation and thus cannot withstand some stringent chemical exposures which are readily resisted by Terylene.   This, in turn, has a limited resistance to alkalis or ammonia which have a lesser effect on nylon and none on polypropylene; the latter, however, melts at a considerably lower temperature than the others and cannot be readily dyed. As compared with the acrylic or poly(vinyl alcohol) fibres, with even the newer cellulose acetates and with cotton or wool, the polyester fibres stand in a different category of durability and shape and properties-retention, although conversely some of these have desirable properties of moisture absorption and handle which are not present in the polyester and which, by fibre blending, provides the textile operator with products combining the useful qualities of both.

A similar situation exists for films. Polyesters are more costly than polyethylene or cellulosic films but are distinguished by their remarkable strength and tear-resistance. Their electrical properties as insulators may be poorer than that of the hydrocarbon films, but in high-temperature performance the polyesters are incomparably superior; likewise, their resistance to the passage of moisture is very much greater than that of the polyamides and cellulose acetate, and in comparison with poly(vinyl chloride) films the freedom from plasticisers can be of special importance.

A number of the materials which have just been compared with the polyesters as film and fibre-forming materials also have value as moulding substances, but the only linear polyesters which have so far shown promise in this direction are certain polycarbonates whose utility is connected with their essentially non-crystallising character in the massive state, allied to the possession of unusually high glass-transition temperatures. No single factor explains the general unsuitability of crystallising polyesters for use as moulding polymers. In the case of the classical aliphatic polyesters (Section 1.2), the typical chemical, thermal, and mechanical properties are at too low a level to provide utility as thermoplastics. Some other polyesters, as will be shown later, are too unstable thermally to be made or processed at the requisite molecular weights. Poly(ethylene terephthalate), which is representative of a number of high-melting crystalline polyesters, is unsuitable as a moulding material owing to the brittleness of the product when the molecularly unoriented polymer solidifies from the molten state. That this should be so when various other types of crystallising polymers are valuable moulding materials is an interesting reflection of differences in the physical characteristics of the substances in question.

From the earlier discussion it will be recalled that, unlike nylon 6.6 and polyethylene, for example, which normally crystallise directly from the melt, poly(ethylene terephthalate) is rather readily quenched to an amorphous state which is metastable with respect to the crystalline material. The technologies of fibre- and film-making from the polyester therefore demand special steps in the control of crystallisation and its development to the equilibrium condition. The circumstances of moulding operations, involving the relatively slow dissipation of heat from the bulk material, do not permit such control but are conducive to the random growth of spherulites in the unoriented material, and thus to the production of a solid inhomogeneous texture where, as a result of the volume contraction on crystallisation from the glassy state, molecular strains are accumulated in the inter-spherulitic material. Because the temperature range of transition from the glassy to the rubbery state in the amorphous component of crystallised poly(ethylene terephthalate) is relatively high compared with that of other common crystallising moulding polymers, and also because its hydrophobic character prevents the broadening of this range by absorption of moisture from the atmosphere (as happens, for example, with the nylons), the frozen-in strains cannot be released by local molecular adjustments and they find outward expression in low brittle-strengths. In agreement with this interpretation it has been claimed that copolymerisation (which normally leads to a higher amorphous content and a more 'open' molecular texture) gives polyesters of better moulding characteristics but, as will be discussed later, the degree of copolymerisation required to produce a sufficient change of behaviour is usually undesirably large, and no successful development of ethylene terephthalate copolymers for moulding applications has been attained.

The polymer technologist will be well aware that there is no universal or ideal fabrication material. Indeed, the uses of polymers are so multifarious that no single substance could conceivably combine the properties requisite to cover all needs. The best that that can be hoped for is selection of the material most apt for a particular purpose. It has already been stressed that the range of technically useful linear polyesters has been extended since the advent of poly(ethylene terephthalate) by only two members, the polycarbonate resins and poly(cyclohexane-1,4-dimethylene terephthalate). In view of the many linear polyesters known, this small number might appear surprising; but there are sound practical reasons for it.

To be fibre-forming at all a polymer must satisfy the basic molecular criterion of being able to accept a permanent and high

Table 3.3 MELTING POINTS (T_m), GLASS-TRANSITION TEMPERATURES (T_g) OR SOFTENING POINTS, AND SOME OTHER PROPERTIES OF CERTAIN POLYESTERS EXAMINED AS FIBRE-FORMING MATERIALS

Polymer Repeat-Unit	T_m(°C)	T_g or S.p.(°C)	Typical tenacity/extension and other fibre properties	References
1 —O·CH$_2$·CO—	220–230°	95°	4–5 g/den; 15–25% Fibres readily hydrolysed	86, 87, 88
2 —O·CMe$_2$·CO—	190°	55–60°	2 g/den; 53% Dissolved by many organic liquids	89
3 —O·CH$_2$·CMe$_2$·CO—	236°	40–45°	1·9 g/den; 20% Thermally unstable and degrades on melt spinning. Fibres shrink 7% at 100°C	88, 90
4 —OC·O·φ·CMe$_2$·φ·O—	220–230° (250° when stretched)	150°	4–6 g/den; 12–25% Embrittled by many organic liquids; chemical resistance in fibrous form limited	88, 93, 94
5 —O·CH$_2$·φ·CO—	240–250°	85–90°	Thermally unstable and degrades on melt-spinning	88, 91, 92
6 —O·(CH$_2$)$_2$·O·OC·φ·(CH$_2$)$_2$·φ·CO—	220°	120°	Poor oxidative stability; tends to cross-link at high temperatures	88
7 —O·(CH$_2$)$_2$·O·OC—⟨φ-R⟩—CO— (a) R=H	215–225°	84°	3·8 g/den; 38% Fibres relax or shrink in boiling water	95–98
(b) R=OMe	260–272°	74°	Degraded by hot water; fibres have poor resistance to abrasion	96–99
8 —O·(CH$_2$)$_2$·O·OC—⟨φ-R⟩—O·(CH$_2$)$_2$·O·OC—⟨φ-R⟩—CO— (a) R=H (b) R=OMe	254°	105–115°	7 g/den; 6% Excellent fibre properties	88, 100
(b) R = OMe	200–210°	S.p. about 80°	4 g/den Fibres shrink on heating	101

Table 3.3—contd.

Polymer Repeat-Unit	$T_m(°C)$	T_g or S.p.(°C)	Typical tenacity/extension and other fibre properties	References
9 —O.CH₂ [benzodioxane ring] CO— (isomer mixture)	200–215°	S.p. about 145°	4·2 g/den; 35%	102
10 —O·(CH₂)$_n$·O·OC·φ·SO₂·φ·CO—				
(a) n = 2	340° (decomp.)		Unspinnable from the melt	103
(b) n = 3	320° (decomp.)		Unspinnable from the melt	103
(c) n = 5	240–250°*		Excellent fibre properties claimed	103
(d) n = 6	270–280°		Excellent fibre properties claimed	103
11 —O·(CH₂)$_n$·O·OC·φ·φ·CO—				
(a) n = 2	> 350° (decomp.)	185°	Unspinnable from the melt	88, 104
(b) n = 3	275–280°	180°	Yields brittle filaments only	88, 104
(c) n = 5	210–217°	130–135°	Yields brittle filaments only	88, 104
(d) n = 6	235–240°	about 150°	Yields brittle filaments only	88, 104
12 OC·O·(CH₂)₃·φ·(CH₂)₃·O—	215°		Yields brittle products only	105
13 —OC·O·CH₂·φ·CH₂·O—	about 250°		Yields brittle products only	106
14 —OC·O·(CH₂)₃·φ·(CH₂)₃·O—	250°		Yields brittle products only	107
15 —O·(CH₂)₂·O.OC [naphthalene] CO—	265–268°	150–180°	5–6 g/den; 10–15% Adequate to good fibre behaviour	88
16 —O·(CH₂)₂.O.OC [furan ring] CO—	215–225°		Polymer thermally unstable	88, 108, 109

* Fibre sticking-temperature: this is generally rather lower than the polymer melting point.

degree of molecular orientation. Experience teaches that this is connected with chain linearity and some degree of symmetry of structure; with the possession of a fair degree of molecular flexibility; often, though not invariably, with the possession or production of crystallinity; and necessarily with an adequate molecular chain-length. The fundamental requirements for the formation of useful orientable films are not so well defined but probably they are broadly similar. These criteria represent the absolute minimum and, of themselves, offer no guarantee of properties of merit. To be of utility a polymer must also lend itself to fabrication without difficulty; it must possess properties which are reasonably constant over a wide range of chemical and thermal exposure conditions, and, if it is to make any commercial impact, its synthesis must be economic and accessible in terms of raw materials. One may conjecture that no new polyester is likely to enter the market successfully without some clear superiority in cost or behaviour over the established materials; this is equally true, of course, for new entrants into any polymer class. Of the whole existing group of linear polyesters, many are excluded from use at the outset by their primary properties. Some are liquid at ordinary temperatures; some, although solid and readily fibre-forming, are too low-melting or too sensitive to solvents or hydrolytic attack to find easy application; at the other end of the scale, some are too insoluble or infusible to be fabricated at all, whilst others are thermally unstable (causing difficulties in polycondensation or during melt-extrusion) or their fibres are insufficiently distinguished to be of interest.

Table 3.3 lists a number of polyesters which have been the subject of some serious study as possible fibre-forming materials in recent years. The table indicates a trend to seek polyesters having high melting points (above 200°C) and high glass-transition temperatures (100°C or upwards), but whilst it is attractive to hope for a higher ceiling of attainable performance than is found in the present-day linear polyesters, there is likely to be an upper limit caused by the general instability of all but a few members of this class at temperatures above 300–320°C.

It is unnecessary to discuss the listed compounds in detail, but a few points will be indicated to illustrate further the argument just made. Poly(dimethyldi-*p*-phenylenemethane carbonate) (Table 3.3 (4)), the best known of the polycarbonates, can be converted to fibres by melt-, dry-, and wet-spinning methods. Although it has a special interest as a moulding and film-forming material, the properties of the fibres are not outstanding, and their ready crystallisation and embrittlement on contact with many organic solvents offers little hope for textile use. The compounds formulated in Table 3.3 (7 b, 8 b, and 9) can be synthesised from some readily available naturally occurring chemical precursors, on which account they have been examined in some detail, but, as the Table shows, they have not yielded fibres of merit. Poly(*p*-methylene-benzoate) (Table 3.3 (5)), poly(ethylene bibenzyl-4,4'-dicarboxylate) (Table 3.3 (6)) and poly(*p*-2-ethyleneoxybenzoate) (Table 3.3 (7 a)) have likewise attracted attention because of their relative accessibility as chemical materials, but their practical behaviour has not justified further development. The ethylene glycol polyesters shown in Table 3.3 (10 a and 11 a) are typical of polymers ostensibly of interest on account of their high melting points but too intractable in properties for conversion to fibres by melt- or solution-spinning. The higher poly(alkylene biphenyl-4,4'-dicarboxylates) (Table 3.3 (11 b, c, and d)), and the polycarbonates (Table 3.3 (12–14)), exemplify yet another type of behaviour defect, namely of crystallising to an unoriented mass with such rapidity that drawing cannot be carried out, and the products are consequently brittle and inextensible.

The solubility of some polyesters in organic liquids, which can limit or even preclude their use as textile fibres, can sometimes be turned to advantage for film-making by solvent-casting, or for coating purposes. Table 3.4 contains examples of some newer polyesters which, it is claimed, can usefully be applied in this way. As with Table 3.3, it aims to display the trend rather than the totality of recent work in this field, and figures of film performance are intentionally omitted since the test data scattered throughout the original publications cannot readily be compared. These substances, some of which are obtained only in amorphous forms, are again of interest on account of their elevated softening or melting points, and it will be noted that the chemical structures depicted mostly have a considerable congestion of groups to which the high softening points may well be due. Certain of these compounds also contain one or more chlorine atoms in their structures, on which account their flammability is greatly reduced. Whether any of these polyesters will ultimately achieve commercial utility remains a matter for the future.

The theme of the foregoing paragraphs has designedly been presented at an empirical level. The next Chapter will outline our knowledge of the relationships between the properties and the molecular structures of polyesters and of their copolymers which

Table 3.4 SOME EXAMPLES OF POLYESTERS EXAMINED AS FILM-FORMING MATERIALS

	Polymer Repeat-Unit	T_m (°C)	T_g (°C) or S.p.	References
1	$—OC·\phi·CMe_2·\phi·CO·O·\phi·CMe_2·\phi·O—$		230°	110, 111, 112
2	$—OC·\phi·CH_2·\phi·CO·O·\phi·CMe_2·\phi·O—$		185°	110, 111, 112
3	$—OC·\phi·O·\phi·CO·O·\phi·CMe_2·\phi·O—$		220°	110, 111, 112
4	$—OC—\langle\text{ring}\rangle—CO·O·\phi·CMe_2·\phi·O—$	240–250°	120–130°	111, 112
5	$—OC·\phi·CO·O·\phi·CMe_2·\phi·O—$	250–300°		113, 114
6	$—OC·\phi·CO·O—\langle\text{Me,Me ring}\rangle—O—$	270–320°	185°	115
7	$—O—\langle\text{Cl,Cl ring}\rangle—O·OC—\langle\text{Cl ring}\rangle—CO—$	285–305°		116, 117
8	$—O·\phi·O·OC—\langle\text{Cl ring}\rangle—CO—$	323–349°		116, 117
9	$—CO·O·(CH_2)_2·O—\langle\text{Cl,Cl ring}\rangle CMe_2 \langle\text{Cl,Cl ring}\rangle—O·(CH_2)_2·O—$	170–190°	80–90°	118

have often been studied in attempts to modify or extend the utility of the parent compounds. It must be stated, however, that despite the extent of this knowledge our ability to predict the detailed behaviour of polyesters from their formulae still amounts to little more than a capacity to suggest that individuals *might* satisfy some sought-after grouping of properties. Certainly the defects and difficulties found for many of the materials included in Table 3.3 could not have been foreseen prior to the event. The concept of the 'tailor-made' polymer still remains very much of an ideal, and the need for experimental test and practical assessment will persist for a long time to come.

REFERENCES

(1) GRIEHL, W., and NEUE, S., *Faserforsch. Textiltech.*, **5**, 423 (1954)
(2) RAVENS, D. A. S., and WARD, I. M., *Trans. Faraday Soc.*, **57**, 150 (1961)
(3) CONIX, A., *Makromol. Chem.*, **26**, 226 (1958)
(4) GAYLORD, N. G., and ROSENBAUM, S., *J. Polymer Sci.*, **39**, 545 (1959)
(5) KOEPP, H. M., and WERNER, H., *Makromol. Chem.*, **32**, 79 (1959)
(6) HASELEY, E. A., *J. Polymer Sci.*, **35**, 309 (1959)
(7) KUZNETSOV, E. V., VIZEL', A. O., SHERMERGORN, I. M., and TYULENEV, S. S., *Vysokomolekul. Soedin.*, **2**, 205 (1960)
(8) TURSKA, E., SKWARSKI, T., and SZAPIRO, S., *J. Polymer Sci.*, **30**, 391 (1958)
(9) FLORY, P. J., *J. Amer. Chem. Soc.*, **62**, 1057 (1940)
(10) BAKER, W. O., FULLER, C. S., and HEISS, J. H., *J. Amer. Chem. Soc.*, **63**, 2142 (1941)
(11) GOODINGS, E. P., 'High Temperature Resistance and Thermal Degradation of Polymers', *Soc. Chem. Ind. Monograph No.* 13, 211 (1961)
(12) RASHBROOK, R. B., and TAYLOR, G. W., *Chem. & Ind.*, 215 (1962)
(13) ALLAN, R. J. P., FORMAN, R. L., and RITCHIE, P. D., *J. Chem. Soc.*, 2717 (1955)
(14) RITCHIE, P. D., 'High Temperature Resistance and Thermal Degradation of Polymers', *Soc. Chem. Ind. Monograph No.* 13, 107 (1961)
(15) ROSS, S. D., COBURN, E. R., LEACH, W. A., and ROBINSON, W. B., *J. Polymer Sci.*, **13**, 406 (1954)
(16) GOODMAN, I., and NESBITT, B. F., *J. Polymer Sci.*, **47**, 423 (1960)
(17) GUFFRIA, R., *J. Polymer Sci.*, **49**, 427 (1961)
(18) KARGIN, V. A., *J. Polymer Sci.*, **30**, 247 (1958)
(19) COBBS, W. H., and BURTON, R. L., *J. Polymer Sci.*, **10**, 275 (1953)
(20) KELLER, A., LESTER, G. R., and MORGAN, L. B., *Phil. Trans. Roy. Soc.*, **A247**, 1 (1954)
(21) MORGAN, L. B., *Phil. Trans. Roy. Soc.*, **A247**, 13 (1954)
(22) HARTLEY, F. D., LORD, F. W., and MORGAN, L. B., *Phil. Trans. Roy. Soc.*, **A247**, 23 (1954)
(23) KELLER, A., *J. Polymer Sci.*, **17**, 291 (1955)
(24) ARNOLD, H., *Kolloidzschr.*, **165**, 35 (1959)
(25) GOLIKE, R. C., and COBBS, W. H., *J. Polymer Sci.*, **54**, 277 (1961)
(26) ZACHMANN, H. G., and STUART, H. A., *Makromol. Chem.*, **41**, 131, 148 (1960)
(27) DAUBENY, R. DE P., BUNN, C. W., and BROWN, C. J., *Proc. Roy. Soc.*, **A226**, 531 (1954)
(28) GRIME, D., and WARD, I. M., *Trans. Faraday Soc.*, **54**, 959 (1958)
(29) MIYAKE, A., *J. Polymer Sci.*, **38**, 479, 497 (1959)
(30) FARROW, G., and WARD, I. M., *Polymer*, **1**, 330 (1960)
(31) THOMPSON, A. B., and WOODS, D. W., *Trans. Faraday Soc.*, **52**, 1383 (1956)

(32) SMITH, C. W., and DOLE, M., *J. Polymer Sci.*, **20**, 37 (1956)
(33) GORBACHEVA, V. O., and MIKHAILOV, N. V., *Kolloidn. Zh.*, **20**, 38 (1958)
(34) EDGAR, O. B., and HILL, R., *J. Polymer Sci.*, **8**, 1 (1952)
(35) TREIBER, E., BERNDT, W., and TOPLAK, H., *Angew. Chem.*, **67**, 69 (1955)
(36) SEIDEL, B., *Z. Elektrochem.*, **62**, 214 (1958)
(37) OSBORN, K. R., *J. Polymer Sci.*, **38**, 357 (1959)
(38) HERRMANN, O., *Angew. Chem.*, **74**, 633 (1962)
(39) MICHAELS, A. S., VIETH, W. R., and BARRIE, J. A., *J. Appl. Phys.*, **34**, 1, 13 (1963)
(40) MARSHALL, I., and THOMPSON, A. B., *J. Appl. Chem.* (London), **4**, 145 (1954)
(41) MARSHALL, I., and THOMPSON, A. B., *Proc. Roy. Soc.*, **A221**, 541 (1954)
(42) THOMPSON, A. B., *J. Polymer Sci.*, **34**, 741 (1959)
(43) FARROW, G., and BAGLEY, J., *Textile Res. J.*, **32**, 587 (1962)
(44) GRUNEWALD, H., *Melliand Textilber.*, **43**, 48 (1962)
(45) MIKHAILOV, N. V., *J. Polymer Sci.*, **30**, 259 (1958)
(46) STUART, H. A., *Kolloidzschr.*, **165**, 3 (1959)
(47) HOSEMANN, R., *Polymer*, **3**, 349 (1962)
(48) JUILFS, J., and BERG, H., *Kolloidzschr*, **179**, 29 (1961)
(49) HEARLE, J. W. S., *J. Textile Inst.* (Proceedings), **53**, 449 (1962)
(50) STATTON, W. O., *J. Polymer Sci.*, **58**, 205 (1962)
(51) GOODMAN, I., *Angew. Chem.*, **74**, 606 (1962)
(52) Unpublished findings of Imperial Chemical Industries Limited, Fibres Division, Research Department, Harrogate
(53) BATEMAN, J., RICHARDS, R. E., FARROW, G., and WARD, I. M., *Polymer*, **1**, 63 (1960)
(54) WARD, I. M., *Trans. Faraday Soc.*, **56**, 648 (1960)
(55) FARROW, G., MCINTOSH, J., and WARD, I. M., *Makromol. Chem.*, **38**, 147 (1960)
(56) WARD, I. M., *Textile Res. J.*, **31**, 650 (1961)
(57) HYNDMAN, D., and ORIGLIO, G. F., *J. Polymer Sci.*, **46**, 259 (1960)
(58) GOODMAN, I., and STIMPSON, J. W., unpublished results
(59) GOODMAN, I., and NESBITT, B. F., *Polymer*, **1**, 384 (1960)
(60) MCMAHON, W., BIRDSALL, H. A., JOHNSON, G. R., and CAMILLI, C. T., *J. Chem. Eng. Data*, **4**, 57 (1959)
(61) DAVIES, T., GOLDSMITH, P. L., RAVENS, D. A. S., and WARD, I. M., *J. Phys. Chem.*, **66**, 175 (1962)
(62) FARROW, G., RAVENS, D. A. S., and WARD, I. M., *Polymer*, **3**, 17 (1962)
(63) BAKER, W. P., *J. Polymer Sci.*, **57**, 993 (1962)
(64) STEPHENSON, C. V., LACEY, J. C., and WILCOX, W. S., *J. Polymer Sci.*, **55**, 477 (1961)
(65) TESZLER, O., and RUTHERFORD, H. A., *Textile Res. J.*, **26**, 796 (1956)
(66) HARMON, D. J., *Textile Res. J.*, **27**, 318 (1957)
(67) COEN, A., *Mater. Plast.*, **24**, 302 (1958)
(68) BOYE, C. A., *J. Polymer Sci.*, **55**, 263, 275 (1961)
(69) MARTIN, E. V., *Textile Res. J.*, **32**, 619 (1962)
(70) SCARLETT, A. C. (E. I. du Pont de Nemours and Company), U.S. Pat. 2,823,421
(71) VISSER, P. J., *Plastica*, **14**, 779, 900 (1961)
(72) KOZLOV, P. V., and BERESTNEVA, G. L., *Vysokomolekul. Soedin.*, **2**, 590 (1960)
(73) BERESTNEVA, G. L., and KOZLOV, P. V., *Vysokomolekul. Soedin.*, **2**, 601 (1960)
(74) BERESTNEVA, G. L., BURSHTEIN, L. L., KOZLOV, P. V., MIKHAILOV, G. P., and NORDBEK, K. E., *Vysokomolekul. Soedin.*, **2**, 1739 (1960)
(75) BERESTNEVA, G. L., BERESTNEV, V. A., GATOVSKAYA, T. V., KARGIN, V. A., and KOZLOV, P. V., *Vysokomolekul. Soedin.*, **3**, 801 (1961)
(76) BERESTNEVA, G. L., TSVANKIN, D. YA., and KOZLOV, P. V., *Vysokomolekul. Soedin.*, **3**, 1787 (1961)
(77) MIKHAILOV, N. V., KLUEVA, O. A., GORBACHEVA, V. O., and FAINBERG, E. Z., *Vysokomolekul. Soedin.*, **2**, 942 (1960)
(78) LIANG, C. Y., and KRIMM, S., *J. Chem. Phys.*, **27**, 327 (1957)

(79) DULMAGE, W. J., and GEDDES, A. L., *J. Polymer Sci.*, **31**, 499 (1958)
(80) HEFFELFINGER, C. J., and BURTON, R. L., *J. Polymer Sci.*, **47**, 289 (1960)
(81) SCHMIDT, P. G., and GAY, F. P., *Angew. Chem.*, **74**, 638 (1962)
(82) TADOKORO, H., TATSUKA, K., and MURAHASHI, S., *J. Polymer Sci.*, **59**, 413 (1962)
(83) REDDISH, W., *Trans. Faraday Soc.*, **46**, 459 (1950)
(84) REDDISH, W., *Pure Appl. Chem.*, **5**, 723 (1962)
(85) WATSON, M. T., *SPE J.*, **17**, 1083 (1961)
(86) BECK, M. L. (E. I. du Pont de Nemours and Co.), U.S. Pat. 2,585,427
(87) LOWE, C. E. (E. I. du Pont de Nemours and Co.), U.S. Pat. 2,668,162
(88) Unpublished observations of the Research Department, Imperial Chemical Industries Limited, Fibres Division, Harrogate
(89) ALDERSON, T. (E. I. du Pont de Nemours and Co.), U.S. Pat. 2,811,511
(90) REYNOLDS, R. J. W., and VICKERS, E. J. (Imperial Chemical Industries Ltd.), Brit. Pat. 766,347
(91) LUDEWIG, H., RAMM, H., and WIEGAND, K., *J. Prakt. Chem.*, [4], **6**, 103 (1958)
(92) ZÁMORSKÝ, Z., and VESELÝ, R., *Chem. Průmysl*, **6/33**, 106 (1958)
(93) Farbenfabriken Bayer, A.G., Brit. Pats. 844,488; 903,603
(94) Kunoshima Kagaku Kogyo Kabushiki Kaisha, French Pats. 1,240,227–8
(95) Kokoku Rayon and Pulp Co. Ltd., Belgian Pat. 560,521
(96) BOCK, L. H. (Rayonier Incorporated), U.S. Pats. 2,686,198; 2,755,273
(97) KOREMATSU, M., MASUDA, H., and KURIYAMA, S., *Kogyo Kagaku Zasshi*, **63**, 884 (1960)
(98) National Rayon Pulp Co. Ltd., Japanese Pat. 9598/59
(99) Inventa A.G. für Forschung und Patentverwertung, French Pat. 1,220,725
(100) DICKSON, J. T., Brit. Pat. 579,462
(101) BOCK, L. H., and ANDERSON, J. K., *J. Polymer Sci.*, **17**, 553 (1955)
(102) Rayonier Incorporated, Brit. Pat. 734,800
(103) CALDWELL, J. R. (Eastman Kodak Co.), U.S. Pat. 2,744,089
(104) WIELICKI, E. A., and EVANS, R. D. (American Viscose Corporation), Brit. Pats. 884,680; 884,049.
(105) REYNOLDS, D. D., and VAN DEN BERGHE, J. (Eastman Kodak Company), U.S. Pats. 2,789,967; 2,789,970
(106) REYNOLDS, D. D., and DUNHAM, K. R. (Eastman Kodak Company), U.S. Pats. 2,789,966; 2,789,969
(107) REYNOLDS, D. D., and DUNHAM, K. R. (Eastman Kodak Company), U.S. Pats. 2,789,971–2
(108) DREWITT, J. G. N., and LINCOLN, J. (Celanese Corporation of America), U.S. Pat. 2,551,731
(109) HACHIHAMA, J., SHONO, T., and HYONO, K., *Technol. Rept. Osaka Univ.*, **8**, 475 (1958) (through *Chem. Abstr.*, **53**, 18933 (1959))
(110) CONIX, A. J. (Gevaert Photo-Producten), Brit. Pat. 883,312
(111) CONIX, A., *Industr. Engng. Chem.*, **51**, 147 (1959)
(112) CONIX, A. J. (Gevaert Photo-Producten), Brit. Pat. 901,605
(113) KORSHAK, V. V., and VINOGRADOVA, S. V., *Russ. Chem. Revs.* (English Trans.), **30**, 171 (1961)
(114) EARECKSON, W. M., *J. Polymer Sci.*, **40**, 399 (1959)
(115) ELAM, E. U., MARTIN, J. C., and GILKEY, R. (Kodak-Pathé), French Pat. 1,278,284
(116) KANTOR, S. W., and HOLUB, F. F. (General Electric Co.), U.S. Pats. 3,036,990–992
(117) Compagnie Française Thomson-Houston (Kantor, S. W., and Holub, F. F.), French Pat. 1,291,265
(118) RINKE, H., and SCHNELL, H. (Farbenfabriken Bayer A.G.), U.S. Pat. 3,062,780

CHAPTER 4

PROPERTIES OF POLYESTERS IN RELATION TO STRUCTURE

4.1 INTRODUCTION

The discussion of polyester properties, which has so far been restricted to the relatively limited group of those which have been considered for commercial application, will now be widened to demonstrate the dependence of certain properties upon chemical structure in the compounds as a class. Ideally, since all matter has a common basis in atoms and their interactions, it should be possible to deduce the properties and behaviour of substances from their structural composition, but since this requires a detailed knowledge of the energetic states and spatial location of all of the component atoms it can only be done with satisfaction for a limited range of properties of relatively simple compounds. For polymeric substances it is still necessary for the most part to acquire knowledge of behaviour—especially of physical properties—by experiment and to interpret it afterwards, but in those directions with which this section will be concerned sufficient is now known to permit a useful, though limited, degree of rationalisation and prediction.

Certain properties of polymers are inherent in the chemical monadic unit and are independent of the molecular size. Colour, for instance, is related to the presence of specific light-absorbing groups whose effect is the same whether combined in mono- or macromolecular environments. The resemblance of the ultra-violet absorption spectrum of poly(ethylene terephthalate) to those of simple terephthalate esters has already been mentioned, and azobenzenedicarboxylate polyesters possess the characteristic red-brown colour of the simple chromophore.[1] Some other properties are inherent but may be modified by the internal structural condition of the polymers; the hydrolysis of ester linkages in polyesters is a case in point, where the barriers to diffusion of reagents may make the reaction much less facile than with simple esters although not altering it in principle. On the other hand, the properties of melting and transition behaviour, viscosity, and the capacity of polyesters for film- and fibre-making are specifically properties of the polymeric state, though they will vary with structure from polymer to polymer.

It is interesting to know at what chain length (or degree of molecularity) a polyester can be regarded as highly polymeric, but this question receives answers which vary with the criterion of judgement. Zahn and co-workers[2-4] investigated the issue by examining individual short-chain linear oligomers of poly(ethylene terephthalate), $X \cdot [O \cdot (CH_2)_2 \cdot O \cdot OC \cdot \phi \cdot CO]_n \cdot Y$, where X and Y were varied groups and n had values from 1 to 5. The densities, melting points, and crystallographic lattice spacings of the lower members of this series were very different from those of the high polymer, but with increase in n the properties altered towards those of the high molecular weight polyester. From this standpoint, highly polymeric character might be thought to be present at a molecularity of, say, 10. These short-chain polyesters, however, are relatively perfectly crystalline bodies whose bulk properties are only indirectly instructive on the nature of materials, like high polymers, having a crystalline/amorphous texture; evidently this approach is incomplete. An alternative is the pragmatic test of determining where, in the molecularity scale, the properties of film- or fibre-formation are first made evident. The now classic work of Carothers and Van Natta[5] with poly(nonamethylene carboxylate) showed that the capacity for fibre formation was first displayed at molecular weights of about 5,000. The resultant filaments were weak and could not be drawn; drawing first became possible at a molecular weight of 10,000, whilst full fibrous character was only obtained at still higher molecular weights (17,000). The minimum molecular weight for fibre formation varies, however, from one polymer to another. For certain hexamethylene alkanedioate polyesters the values have been shown to be as low as 12,000 and as high as 28,000 for others,[6,7] whereas for poly(ethylene terephthalate) it lies at about 4,000–5,000.

From these and other considerations the conclusion is drawn that some properties, such as the melting point and glass-transition temperature, are virtually independent of molecularity above a certain level; that some, such as the viscosities of melts or solutions, increase constantly with increase in molecular weight; and that others, including the capacity for orientation, are correlated with the presence of an amorphous component in which chain entanglement can occur, and only appear at a level of some thousands of units of molecular weight, thereafter remaining moderately constant over a considerable range.

4.2 THE MELTING POINTS OF CRYSTALLINE POLYESTERS: GENERAL REMARKS

The practical importance of melting points in relation to the fabrication and use of polyesters has already been discussed, but knowledge of melting temperatures also provides insight into some aspects of the molecular condition of the polymers which must now be explained.

From what was said earlier about the structure and conformation of crystalline polyesters, e.g. poly(ethylene terephthalate), it will be understood that the events during melting involve a change from a more ordered to a less ordered state. At this point in the temperature scale, the forces of thermal vibration of the molecules, expressed in local dislocations and segmental motions, exceed the crystal lattice energy, so that the detailed spacing and alignment of polymer chains breaks down and the crystalline parts liquefy. In principle these events are reversed upon cooling, even though it may happen in practice that recrystallisation is delayed owing to supercooling or the disappearance of nuclei. Theoretically, we can define the melting point T_m as the temperature where the liquid and solid states of the polymer can coexist in equilibrium, and, by thermodynamic reasoning, at equilibrium we have the relation $T_m = \Delta H / \Delta S$, where ΔH and ΔS represent the heat and entropy of melting, respectively. The maintenance of the solid state of crystalline polymers is supported by a number of molecular factors which can be divided qualitatively into two groups, (*a*) cohesive forces between molecules, due to the van der Waals forces and the mutual attraction of dipoles and ionic sites, when these are present, and (*b*) inertial forces which resist changes in the positions and configurations of those segments of the molecules which are in the crystalline lattice. These factors find reflection, even if not direct equivalence, in the heat and entropy of melting, and the latter is also affected by the regularity of molecular arrangement and by molecular symmetry. It is thus apparent that melting point comparisons offer a means of comparing the balance between these fundamental molecular properties. There are very few polyesters for which both ΔH and ΔS are known, so that the discussion has to remain qualitative and speculative in the present state of knowledge, but the generally systematic response of T_m to changes of molecular structural pattern allows one to extrapolate from the melting points of known polyesters to those of new ones with some degree of confidence, and also makes it possible to attempt reasoned molecular interpretations for the occasional result which apparently deviates from the normal.

Polyesters do not melt as sharply as monomolecular substances: the process normally occurs over a range of a few Centigrade degrees, and the apparent T_m can be affected by the rate of heating of the polymer, by its previous thermal history, and by the method of measurement. Impurities and trace foreign components copolymeric in the main structure can also affect the result, and values quoted here, or in the literature, for polymers which have not been repeatedly and extensively characterised should be regarded as subject to an uncertainty of, say, ± 3–$4°C$. Melting points can be determined by a number of methods, e.g. penetrometry, differential thermal analysis, X-ray diffraction methods, and visual observations. For the comparison and characterisation of a wide range of polymers, a convenient and reliable procedure is the observation of annealed samples, as thin films or powders, heated slowly at a standard rate on the stage of a polarising microscope, when the temperature of disappearance of birefringence is noted. Alternatively, one may determine the temperature at which the material melts on, or adheres to, a heated metal surface, or at which a stressed film or fibre suddenly elongates or breaks. Which method is adopted depends on the purpose and accuracy required of the determination, but simple capillary-type methods, as commonly used with monomolecular materials, are not recommended since molten polymers are often too viscous to collapse sharply to an identifiable liquid phase. It is again emphasised that what is discussed here is the melting of crystalline polyesters and not the softening of amorphous ones, which is more properly the glass/rubber transition. Whenever the crystalline state of a polymer is in doubt, it should be checked at least by testing for birefringence and preferably by X-ray diffraction. Failure to distinguish crystalline from amorphous polymers has been responsible for much confusion in the literature.

4.2.1 EFFECTS OF HOMOLOGATION AND RING-INCLUSION

The most typical and basic patterns of T_m/structure relationships are seen in Fig. 4.1 composed from data in the literature and from work in the author's laboratory. This brings together melting point values for a number of polyesters comprising several distinct linear-chain homologous series; the melting point of polymethylene, $[—CH_2—]_n$, a convenient reference substance, is inserted as a guide line across the diagram.

Examination of the various series reveals several definite trends:

(*a*) the polyesters of all-aliphatic structure are lower-melting than polymethylene (some exceptions, not shown in Fig. 4.1, are discussed later), but T_m tends to increase as the series are ascended,

(*b*) polyesters containing cyclic structural components, whether in the moieties derived from diol or dicarboxylic acid, are generally higher-melting than polymethylene, but T_m decreases as the methylene contents of the repeat units increase,

(*c*) in all series there is a marked zig-zag pattern of alternation of T_m between the homologues of odd and even chain-atom number, the odd members forming lower-melting groups than the even ones,

(*d*) from the general form of the curves, all series might be expected to converge upon the polymethylene value if extended to sufficiently high methylene contents, but some of the series show signs of a fall to a minimum level of T_m prior to this convergence. These results are supported by the additional data of Table 4.1 for groups of polyesters of more complex structures, and of those derived from hydroxy-acids.

If the poly(alkylene adipates) (Fig. 4.1, Curve 6) are compared with the analogous terephthalates (Curve 3), it can be seen that a marked elevation of melting point occurs in each pair when the unit $(CH_2)_4$ is replaced by ϕ. This, of course, was the substance of Whinfield and Dickson's discovery in 1941, and for at least a decade thereafter it was customary to explain this effect by reference to two supposed special factors. The first postulated the presence of special forces of intermolecular attraction which were supposed to operate between benzene rings in adjacent chains, while the other invoked chemical resonance theory with the suggestion that the whole terephthalate unit $[—O_2C\cdot\phi\cdot CO_2—]$ was rigid and irrotatable

Table 4.1 THE MELTING POINTS OF CERTAIN POLYESTERS

Series	T_m(°C) for n =										
	0	1	2	3	4	5	6	7	8	9	10
1	—	—	254	190	220	150	170	—	—	—	—
2	—	—	254	160	188	100	170	—	—	—	135
3	—	—	265	—	320	—	155	—	220	—	125
4	225	172	125	115	—	—	—	—	—	—	—
5	> 300	—	270	213	230	175	181	—	143	—	182
6	—	—	273	—	—	—	240	—	—	—	182
7	—	—	82	—	86	84	90	—	—	—	98
8	—	—	17	29	67	30	47	—	—	—	61
9	—	225	122	—	53	55	52	—	66	76	74
10	230	—	66	—	125	—	57	—	73	—	53
11	—	—	188	—	185	164	167	—	—	—	156
12	—	—	220	150	170	—	160	—	—	—	—

Series   Unit Structure

1. Poly(ethylene alkylenedioxy-4,4'-dibenzoates)
$$—O \cdot (CH_2)_2 \cdot O \cdot OC \cdot \phi \cdot O \cdot (CH_2)_n \cdot O \cdot \phi \cdot CO—$$
2. Poly(alkylene diphenoxyethane-4,4'-dicarboxylates)
$$—O \cdot (CH_2)_n \cdot O \cdot OC \cdot \phi \cdot O \cdot (CH_2)_2 \cdot O \cdot \phi \cdot CO—$$
3. Poly(p-phenylenedialkyl terephthalates)
$$—O \cdot (CH_2)_{n/2} \cdot \phi \cdot (CH_2)_{n/2} \cdot O \cdot OC \cdot \phi \cdot CO—$$
4. Poly(p-2-ethyleneoxyphenyl alkanoates)
$$—O \cdot (CH_2)_2 \cdot O \cdot \phi \cdot (CH_2)_n \cdot CO—$$
5. Poly(1,4-*trans*-cyclohexylene alkanedioates)
$$—O \cdot C_6H_{10} \cdot O \cdot OC \cdot (CH_2)_n \cdot CO—$$
6. Poly(alkylene dianilinoethane-4,4'-dicarboxylates)
$$—O \cdot (CH_2)_n \cdot O \cdot OC \cdot \phi \cdot NH \cdot (CH_2)_2 \cdot NH \cdot \phi \cdot CO—$$
7. Poly(alkylene sulphonyl-4,4'-divalerates)
$$—O \cdot (CH_2)_n \cdot O \cdot OC \cdot (CH_2)_4 \cdot SO_2 \cdot (CH_2)_4 \cdot CO—$$
8. Poly(alkylene diglycollates)
$$—O \cdot (CH_2)_n \cdot O \cdot OC \cdot CH_2 \cdot O \cdot CH_2 \cdot CO—$$
9. Poly(alkylene carboxylates) $$—(CH_2)_n CO \cdot O—$$
10. Poly(p-phenylenedialkyl adipates)
$$—O \cdot (CH_2)_{n/2} \cdot \phi \cdot (CH_2)_{n/2} \cdot O \cdot OC \cdot (CH_2)_4 \cdot CO—$$
11. Poly(alkylene ethylenedisulphonyl-4,4'-divalerates)
$$—O \cdot (CH_2)_n \cdot O \cdot OC \cdot (CH_2)_4 \cdot SO_2 \cdot (CH_2)_2 \cdot SO_2 \cdot (CH_2)_4 \cdot CO—$$
12. Poly(ethylene alkylene-4,4'-dibenzoates)
$$—O \cdot (CH_2)_2 \cdot O \cdot OC \cdot \phi \cdot (CH_2)_n \cdot \phi \cdot CO—$$

Note that in series 3 and 10 the value of n in the table is the total number of methylene groups in the glycol portion of the repeat-unit.

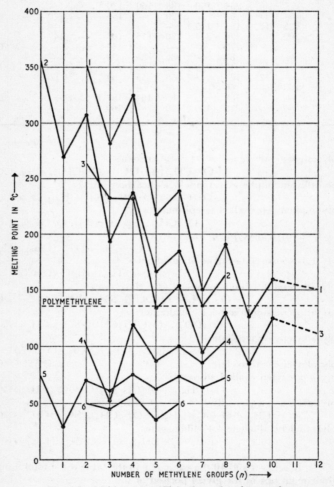

	SERIES	REPEAT–UNIT STRUCTURES
(1)	POLY (ALKYLENE BIPHENYL–4,4'–DICARBOXYLATES)	$-O\cdot(CH_2)_n\cdot O\cdot OC$ ⬡⬡ $CO-$
(2)	POLY (p–PHENYLENE ALKANEDIOATES)	$-O$ ⬡ $O\cdot OC\cdot(CH_2)_n\cdot CO-$
(3)	POLY (ALKYLENE TEREPHTHALATES)	$-O\cdot(CH_2)_n\cdot O\cdot OC$ ⬡ $CO-$
(4)	POLY (ALKYLENE SUCCINATES)	$-O\cdot(CH_2)_n\cdot O\cdot OC\cdot(CH_2)_2CO-$
(5)	POLY (DECAMETHYLENE ALKANEDIOATES)	$-O\cdot(CH_2)_{10}O\cdot OC\cdot(CH_2)_nCO-$
(6)	POLY (ALKYLENE ADIPATES)	$-O\cdot(CH_2)_n\cdot O\cdot OC\cdot(CH_2)_4CO-$

Fig. 4.1   Melting points (T_m) of some homologous polyesters

owing to a supposed enforced coplanarity of the ester groups with the central ring. The first view was no longer tenable after the elucidation of the crystal structure,[8] which showed the molecular chains to be separated by the normal distances rather than by the closer spacings which would ensue from the play of special forces. The second view appears today to be neither exact nor necessary;[9,10] high melting points, involving comparable increases as compared with acyclic analogues, occur when benzenoid rings having no extended extra-nuclear resonance are present in polyester chains (see Fig. 4.1 curve 2, and Table 4.1, series 3), and similar results follow the insertion of heterocyclic or of non-resonant alicyclic rings of suitable symmetry into, or in place of, linear chain segments as exemplified in Table 4.2.

By introducing a higher proportion of cyclic structures, T_m can be increased still further; Curves 1 and 3 of Fig. 4.1 show this as a result of the replacement of —ϕ— by —$\phi \cdot \phi$—, and it will again be noted that the gap between the two series tends to narrow as the methylene content is increased. In the limit, polyesters such as $[-O \cdot \phi \cdot CO-]_n$ or $[-O \cdot \phi \cdot O \cdot OC \cdot \phi \cdot CO-]_n$ prove to be virtually infusible (being solid to above 360°C in both cases), as do the analogues which have *trans*-1,4-cyclohexylene groups in the place of p-phenylene.[12] Such polymers can change configuration, if at all, only at the ester groups.

It is now generally accepted that these effects reflect differences in the segmental molecular mobilities of the polymers. A polyester containing the p-phenylene group (—ϕ—) is incapable, over the axial length of this entity, of the rotatory movements and the possibilities for configurational change which are present in an analogue having —$(CH_2)_4$— in a similar position; likewise for the biphenylylene group (—$\phi \cdot \phi$—) in place of the chain-equivalent —$(CH_2)_8$—. This effect of 'chain-stiffening', which was postulated as the main source of the high melting point of Terylene by Edgar and Hill in 1952,[17] is encountered throughout the whole of polymer chemistry, and it has been discussed by several investigators[18,19,20,21] from the standpoint of the heats and entropies of fusion of polyesters.

Considering first the low melting points of the majority of aliphatic polyesters as compared with polymethylene, it is known that the CH_2—O bond, and probably CO—O, requires less energy for rotation than does CH_2—CH_2; moreover, the stabilisation inherent in the preferred conformation of the last-mentioned is lacking at each ester group position in the chain, and the very presence of these groups represents an irruption into the state of

Table 4.2 THE EFFECTS OF REPLACING LINEAR CHAIN-SEGMENTS IN POLYESTERS BY MISCELLANEOUS CYCLIC UNITS

(Melting points in °C)

Parent structure	Derived cyclic structure	Ref.
—OC·φ·CO·O·CH₂·CH₂·CH₂·CH₂·CH₂·CH₂·O— 154°	—OC·φ·CO·O·CH₂CH⟨CH₂.CH₂ / CH₂.CH₂⟩CH.CH₂O— trans 320°	11
	—OC·φ·CO·O·CH₂CH⟨O·CH₂ / CH₂.O⟩CH.CH₂O— trans 295–305°	13
—O·(CH₂)₁₀·O·O·OC·φ·NH·CH₂·CH₂·NH·φ·CO— 182°	—O·(CH₂)₁₀·O·OC·φ·N⟨CH₂·CH₂ / CH₂·CH₂⟩N·φ·CO— 244–248°	14

Table 4.2—cont.

Parent structure	Derived cyclic structure	Ref.
—O·(CH₂)₂·O·OC·CH₂·CH₂·CH₂·CH₂·CO— 52°	$\longrightarrow$ —O·(CH₂)₂·O·OC $\diagdown$ S $\diagup$ CO— 180–190°	15
	$\longrightarrow$ —O·(CH₂)₂·O·OC $\diagdown$ N—NH $\diagup$ CO— 200–210°	15
—O·(CH₂)₄·CO— 53°	$\longrightarrow$ —O·CH $\diagup$CH₂.CH₂$\diagdown$ CH.CO— $\diagdown$CH₂,CH₂$\diagup$ *trans* > 340°	12
	$\longrightarrow$ —O.CH $\diagup$CH₂CH$\diagdown$ CH. CO— $\diagdown$CH₂.CH₂$\diagup$CH.CH₂ 230–240°	16

molecular regularity. Although there must be some degree of inter-chain cohesion of carbonyl dipoles which is absent from the paraffinic polymer, a marked lowering of the heat of fusion is found in the polyesters, and whilst ΔS is also somewhat reduced the nett effect is of reduction in T_m. When benzene rings replace $(CH_2)_n$ segments in the polyester chain there is very little effect upon the heats of fusion of the molar repeat units, thus confirming that no special forces of attraction are introduced; but the entropies of fusion are lowered considerably with respect to the acyclic analogues, so yielding the higher melting points. It is interesting that, in the limited number of cases where the melting points of polyesters can be compared with those of polyethers (i.e. CO—O replaced by CH_2—O), the latter are somewhat the lower melting. The corresponding comparison of polyesters with polysulphonamides and polycarboxamides (CO—O replaced by SO_2—NH and CO—NH) gives melting points which increase in the order stated. Flory, Bedon, and Keefer[20] state that, despite the presence of hydrogen-bonding in the polycarboxamides, these have, in fact, lower molar heats of fusion than the polyesters, and that their considerably higher melting points are due to much lower melting entropies. Tables 3.3 and 4.1 contain examples of polyesters having sulphonyl ($—SO_2—$) groups which evoke a characteristic increase of T_m as compared with the methylene analogues, probably owing to the very strong dipole forces which augment molecular cohesion.

4.2.2 EFFECTS OF SYMMETRY IN THE REPEAT-UNIT STRUCTURES

In Table 4.1 series 3, is shown the melting point (320°C) of poly(p-phenylenediethyl terephthalate), a substance having p-linked cyclic groups in both parts of the repeat unit. Replacement of either of these by a m-phenylene group causes a large fall in melting point (poly(p-phenylenediethyl isophthalate), 139–141°C; poly(m-phenylenediethyl terephthalate) ,155–157°C[22]). When *both* cyclic groups are of the m-form, the polyester is obtained only as an amorphous resin, softening at about 80°C.

This change, of the lowering of melting point, is a normal result of the replacement of a linear structural element of a polyester by an isomeric group of lower symmetry. Thus, the m-analogue of Table 3.3 (7a) melts at 167–169°C,[23] and poly(ethylene isophthalate) at 240°C; poly(ethylene phthalate), having a still more pronounced departure from linear symmetry, melts at 110° C.[2]

Replacements of this type are often associated with a marked decrease in the ease of crystallisation, sometimes to the point of extinction, and with a reduced ease of orientation, so that fibre- and film-formation is less facile with such polymers than with their more linear analogues.

The effect is also produced by other symmetry-structural changes than those just exemplified. Binuclear compounds can be illustrated in the ethylene polyesters of the naphthalene-2,6-, 2,7-, 1,5- and 1,4-dicarboxylic acids, whose melting points fall in the order given, and in the biphenyl-3,3'-dicarboxylic and diphenyl sulphone 3,3'-dicarboxylic polyesters, which are likewise lower-melting and of poorer fibre-forming propensity than their 4,4'-analogues.[25-27] Similar changes follow the replacement of (*a*) *trans*-cyclohexane rings in polyesters by their *cis*-isomers (e.g. all-*trans* isomer of Fig. 1.4 (b), m.p. 320°C; all-*cis*, Fig. 1.4 (b), m.p. 260°C),[12,28] (*b*) 1,4-linked 6-membered rings by 5- or 7-membered rings,[14] (*c*) *trans*-vinylene groups by *cis*,[29] (*d*) a D-enantiomorph by its *meso* form.[31]

In a discussion, now some years old, of the significance of the *meta/para* relationship, Bunn[26] postulated that molecules of lower symmetry should have the higher entropies of fusion, a view which has since been substantiated by Conix and Van Kerpel's determination of the heats and entropies of fusion of poly(tetramethylene terephthalate) and its lower-melting isophthalate isomer.[30] Curiously, the isophthalate polyester has higher values for both ΔH and ΔS, although the latter is proportionately more increased, yielding the lower melting point. The crystal structure of the isophthalate is unknown, so that a realistic discussion of its molecular packing and configuration is not yet possible, but one may suggest some factors which may be involved.

$$—O \cdot CH_2 \cdot CH_2 \cdot CH_2 \cdot CH_2 \cdot O \cdot OC— \langle\!\langle \bigcirc \rangle\!\rangle —CO—$$

The repeat-unit (above) has a protuberance at one side due to the 'exposed' portion of the benzene ring. For the regular packing of such units, a more specific—and hence less probable—mode of presentation of segments, both in space and time, must be attained than for the terephthalate where several equivalent modes can exist. Once in a lattice, the protuberances may have greater spatial requirements than with the *p*-isomer, possibly giving a less closely-packed structure with weaker crystal bonding forces due to the

lacunae.   The siting of groups on the benzene rings of the isophthalate gives a concentration of dipoles on only one side of the ring,
whilst the other has a hydrogen 'shell' with a reduced tendency to
interact with dipolar forces in neighbouring chains.   More detailed
information is obviously required to assess these factors in detail,
but the great importance of molecular shape and symmetry in
relation to polyester properties is clearly expressed in these examples.

4.2.3   THE EFFECTS OF SUBSTITUTION OF GROUPS FOR HYDROGEN

When hydrogen atoms attached to polyester structures are replaced
by other atoms or groups, the melting points of the new polymers,
provided that these are crystalline, are almost invariably different
from those of the parent compounds.   The differences can be quite
large and may involve either increases or decreases, depending on
the particular molecular or structural environments in which the
change is made;   the same replacement in different parts of a single
repeat-unit can produce opposite results.   Substitution effects
therefore cannot be considered without reference to the situation
in which they occur, and it is as well to state at the outset that
some defy interpretation at the present time.

Most commonly, substitution may cause one of two effects.   In
the first, and most drastic, the substituted polyester is structurally
asymmetric with respect to its parent, in which case crystallisation
will not occur.   Ring-substituted poly(ethylene terephthalates)
(Fig. 3.9, R = Me, OMe, Cl, Br, etc.) exemplify this point, and
similar behaviour is shown by their analogues having asymmetric
substitution in the aliphatic parts of the molecules, e.g.:

$$[-OC \cdot \phi \cdot CO \cdot O \cdot CHMe \cdot CH_2 \cdot O-]_n$$

and

$$[-OC \cdot \phi \cdot CO \cdot O \cdot CH_2 \cdot CH_2 \cdot CHMe \cdot O-]_n$$

Because of the irregularity of directions of combination of
successive units, which may be joined in a 'head-to-head' or
'head-to-tail' sense, such polyesters are normally amorphous resins,
although it will be shown in Section 4.3 that, at an appropriate
degree of overall molecular complexity, crystallinity may be
reasserted despite the randomness of group placements.

The second common effect of substitution, where the symmetry
and capacity for crystallisation are undisturbed, is simply to lower
the melting point.   Thus, poly(ethylene 2,5-dimethylterephtha-
late) melts at 175–185°C, and poly(ethylene 2,3-dimethyltereph-
thalate), a somewhat less symmetrical isomer, at 150–155°C as

compared with 264°C for the parent compound.[32] Similarly referring to Table 3.3, (8 (b)) is lower-melting than (8 (a)), and Fig. 4.2 (a) of analogous structure also melts lower, at 210°C.[33] These results can be interpreted as due to the greater spatial demands of the substituent groups over the hydrogen atom, so that the distances between the polymer-chain skeleta in side-by-side placement are widened, and the resultant intermolecular forces (which are inversely related to certain mathematical powers of the

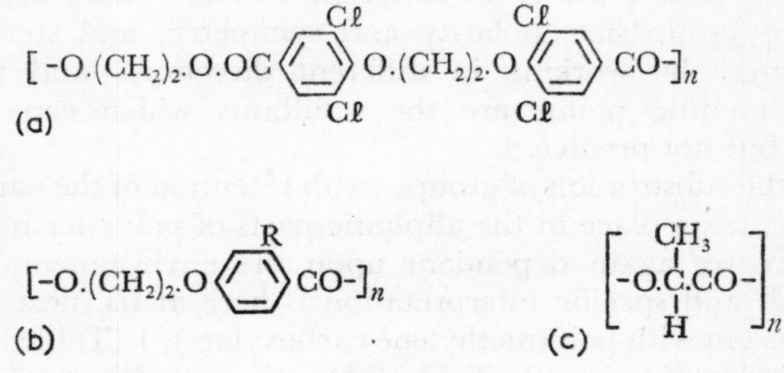

$$[\text{-O.(CH}_2)_2.\text{O.OC} \underset{C\ell}{\overset{C\ell}{\bigcirc}} \text{O.(CH}_2)_2.\text{O} \underset{C\ell}{\overset{C\ell}{\bigcirc}} \text{CO-]}_n$$

(a)

$$[\text{-O.(CH}_2)_2.\text{O} \overset{R}{\bigcirc} \text{CO-]}_n \qquad \left[\text{-O.}\underset{H}{\overset{CH_3}{\underset{|}{\overset{|}{C}}}}.\text{CO-}\right]_n$$

(b)   (c)

Fig. 4.2

distances separating the interacting features) are slightly weakened. This postulated increase in separation has in fact been observed in the crystals of the ethylene 2,5-disubstituted terephthalate poly-esters,[32] where the lateral dimension of the unit cell is dilated as compared with Terylene.

This effect of group-size on polyester melting point is perceptible only where no other more powerful factors are operative. Compound Table 3.3 (7 b), apparently similarly related to Table 3.3 (7 a) to the cases just discussed, is, in fact, higher-melting, and where R in Table 3.3 (7) is Cl or Me the melting points are still higher (280–285°C and 290–292°C, respectively).[34] On the other hand, the isomeric polymers, Fig. 4.2 (b), differing only in the positions occupied by the groups R, melt at 150–153°C for R=Cl and 155–157°C for R=Me, i.e. lower than Table 3.3 (7) R=H, and in accordance with normal expectation. These findings have been interpreted in terms of the details of molecular geometry involved, since the presence of a group R in Table 3.3 (7) impedes rotation of the ethylenedioxy segment by steric collision between R and the hydrogen atoms of the CH_2 group nearest to the ring.[9] In Fig. 4.2 (b) the ester group can rotate around the ϕ—CO_2 axis without interference from Cl or Me so that these are free to exert their 'normal' effect. A larger group may restrict the ease of rotation even in this position, which is probably the reason why poly(ethylene 2,5-dibromoterephthalate) is somewhat higher melting (185–190°C) than its dichloro isomer;[32] Table 4.3 shows further instances of melting point increases resulting from substitution in rings, probably due to the same cause.

In the light of this discussion it may be asked why 8 (b) (Table 3.3) and Fig. 4.2 (a) are lower-melting than their parent 8 (a) (Table 3.3). The answer to this is frankly speculative in indicating that in complex cases a number of different factors (chain separation, substituent group size, polarity and symmetry, and steric interference) may be working in different directions, and that the recorded melting points are the resultants which can only be observed but not predicted.

When the substitution of groups (with retention of the capacity to crystallise) takes place in the aliphatic parts of polyester molecules, the effects are again dependent upon the environmental details concerned, and specific interpretation is here at its most difficult. We may begin with poly(methylene carboxylate), 1 (Table 3.3), and its dimethyl derivative, 2 (Table 3.3), whose melting point is the lower. Structurally intermediate between them is poly(ethylidene carboxylate) or polylactide Fig. 4.2 (c), which is capable of optical isomerism but whose all-L enantiomorph (T_m in the range 160–176°C)[40,41] is the proper form for reference. It might seem that these polyesters are readily understood in terms of the reduced symmetry of Fig. 4.2 (c) and the increased chain-separation of this and 2 (Table 3.3) as compared with 1 (Table 3.3), but the high melting points of the group as a whole, and particularly of 1 (Table 3.3), are themselves so anomalous that this comparison must be regarded with reserve.

Substitution in the next homologue, poly(ethylene carboxylate), leads generally to increases in melting point as summarised in Table 4.4. The effects of symmetry factors in those of the compounds having non-identical alkyl groups, and of cyclisation in the lateral grouping, are well brought out and the series is fascinating for the revelation of the high levels of T_m attainable in aliphatic polyesters of congested structures. Most of the changes, as compared with the parent substance, are explicable on the basis of the enhancement of energy barriers impeding rotation around single bonds—a normal expectation from substitution—but the most substituted member, poly(tetramethylethylene carboxylate), is not, as would have been expected, the highest-melting. It is possible, though there is no evidence for this, that this compound belongs to a

Table 4.3 ELEVATIONS OF MELTING POINTS BY RING-SUBSTITUTION IN POLYESTERS INVOLVING STERIC HINDRANCE TO ROTATION

Repeat-Unit	T_m(°C)	Reference
$-OC.\phi.CO.O.(CH_2)_2O\langle\bigcirc\rangle O.(CH_2)_2.O-$	196°	35
$-OC.\phi.CO.O.(CH_2)_2O\langle\bigcirc\rangle O.(CH_2)_2.O-$ (t-Bu, t-Bu)	212–217°	36
$-O.CH_2\langle\bigcirc\rangle CH_2.CO-$	182–190°	37
$-O.CH_2\langle\bigcirc\rangle CH_2.CO-$ (Me, Me)	220–222°	37
$-O.CH_2\langle\bigcirc\rangle CH_2.CO-$ (Me Me / Me Me)	325–327° (decomp.)	37
$-O.(CH_2)_2.O.OC\langle\bigcirc\rangle CO-$	108–110°	24
$-O.(CH_2)_2.O.OC\langle\bigcirc\rangle CO-$ (Cl Cl / Cl Cl)	163–165°	24
$-OC.(CH_2)_4.CO.O.CH_2\langle\bigcirc\rangle CH_2.O-$	78–81°	38
$-OC.(CH_2)_4.CO.O.CH_2\langle\bigcirc\rangle CH_2.O-$ (Me Me / Me Me)	> 240°	39

Table 4.4 EFFECTS OF SUBSTITUTION ON THE MELTING POINTS OF POLY(ETHYLENE CARBOXYLATES)

(T_m in °C)
(Refs. 42–47)

$-CH_2 \cdot CH_2 \cdot CO \cdot O-$	122°	$-CH_2 \cdot \underset{\displaystyle Et}{\overset{\displaystyle Me}{C}} \cdot CO \cdot O-$	125°
$-CH_2 \cdot \underset{\displaystyle Me}{\overset{\displaystyle Me}{C}} \cdot CO \cdot O-$	236–245°	$-CH_2 \cdot \underset{\displaystyle Pr}{\overset{\displaystyle Et}{C}} \cdot CO \cdot O-$	209°
$-CH_2 \cdot \underset{\displaystyle Et}{\overset{\displaystyle Et}{C}} \cdot CO \cdot O-$	230·5°	$-CH_2.\underset{\displaystyle CH_2-CH_2}{\overset{\displaystyle CH_2-CH_2}{C}}.CO.O- \; CH_2$	260–270°
$-CH_2 \cdot \underset{\displaystyle Bu}{\overset{\displaystyle Bu}{C}} \cdot CO \cdot O-$	245°	$-CH_2 \cdot \underset{\displaystyle Bu}{\overset{\displaystyle Et}{C}} \cdot CO \cdot O-$	180°
$-CH_2 \cdot \underset{\displaystyle CH_2Cl}{\overset{\displaystyle CH_2Cl}{C}} \cdot CO \cdot O-$	295–302°	$-\underset{\displaystyle Me}{\overset{\displaystyle Me}{C}}-\underset{\displaystyle Me}{\overset{\displaystyle Me}{C}} \cdot CO \cdot O-$	165°

different crystallographic family, in which case direct comparison could be misleading.

The regularities suggested in these cases do not find systematic following in the neopentylene polyesters (Fig. 4.3 (a)) in comparison with their unsubstituted trimethylene analogues (Fig. 4.3 (b)).

$$[-OC \cdot R \cdot CO \cdot O \cdot CH_2 \cdot CMe_2 \cdot CH_2 \cdot O-]_n$$

(a)

$$[-OC \cdot R \cdot CO \cdot O \cdot CH_2 \cdot CH_2 \cdot CH_2 \cdot O-]_n$$

(b)

Fig. 4.3

The neopentylene polyesters of terephthalic, biphenyl-4,4'-dicarboxylic, diphenyl sulphone 4,4'-dicarboxylic, and 4,6-dihydroxyisophthalic acids all melt lower (by from 20°C to over 100°C) than the straight-chain members.[48-50] On the other hand, the malonic and succinic polyesters melt higher by 33–34°C, and that of *trans*-cyclohexane-1,4-dicarboxylic acid by 90°C, than the trimethylene analogues whilst poly(neopentylene dimethylmalonate) melts at 271–275°C in contrast to poly(trimethylene malonate), m.p. 33°C.[31,51] Furthermore, in the series shown in Fig. 4.3 (a) and (b) where the acid components are alkanedioic acids, i.e. $R = (CH_2)_n$, then the neopentylene polyesters are the higher-melting when $n = 0$, 1, and 2, but the order is reversed when $n = 4 - 8$.

4.2.4 MISCELLANEOUS GROUP AND STRUCTURAL EFFECTS

Some further types of structural alterations are possible in linear polyesters, and their effects on melting points will be discussed briefly.

(a) Fluorination

The effect of replacement of hydrogen atoms in polyesters by fluorine should logically form part of the discussion on substitution, dealt with in the preceding Section, but on account of the present-day interest in fluorocarbon polymers it is treated separately here, although of little practical importance. Schweiker and Robitschek[52] obtained polyesters of the types shown on the next page

$$[-OC \cdot (CH_2)_x \cdot CO \cdot O \cdot CH_2 \cdot (CF_2)_y \cdot CH_2 \cdot O-]_n$$

and

$$[-OC \cdot (CF_2)_4 \cdot CO \cdot O \cdot CH_2(CF_2)_x \cdot CH_2 \cdot O-]_n$$

which mostly proved to be waxy or crystalline substances having melting points in the range of 30–60°C, just slightly higher than their hydrogen analogues. This suggests that fluorine has little or no specific effect upon T_m, and the few instances of fluorinated ring-containing polyesters for which the melting points are known confirm this.[48,53,54] One patent specification mentions the preparation of poly(tetrafluoro-*p*-phenylene carboxylate) but gives no account of its properties.[55]

(b) Effects of double and triple bonds in the polymer chain

As compared with the ethylene group, $-CH_2\overset{a}{-}CH_2-$, the linkage $-CH\overset{a}{=}CH\overset{b}{-}$ is irrotatable around the bond *a*, and otherwise analogous polymers having ethylene or vinylene groups would be expected to differ in the ease of configurational change and hence of melting point, the olefinic substances being the higher melting. Vinylene groups, however, may be of the *cis*

or *trans*

$$(\diagdown CH = CH \diagup)$$

$$(\diagdown CH = CH \diagdown)$$

isomeric form which differ considerably in shape and symmetry, and, as already noted, the former, as part of a polyester structure, is prone to create low melting points or an inability to crystallise. *trans*-Ethenoid groups, on the other hand, fit more readily into the general shape of a linear hydrocarbon chain-segment and commonly cause an increase in T_m. For aliphatic polyesters the increase may only be small,[7,29] and there is one recorded instance where the unsaturated polymer poly(*trans*-but-2-enylene fumarate) appears to be somewhat lower-melting than its saturated analogue;[56] but the material described was of such low molecular weight that the plateau of variation of T_m with chain length may not have been reached. On the other hand it cannot be ignored that whilst bond *a* of the vinylene group is stiffened, the adjacent bond *b* is more easily rotated, so that a balance of opposing actions may again be involved. When the $-CH_2-CH_2-$ grouping between the benzene rings of (Table 3.3 (6)) is replaced by vinylene to give the polyester $[-O \cdot (CH_2)_2 \cdot O \cdot OC \cdot \phi \cdot CH = CH \cdot \phi \cdot CO-]_n$, an extended rigid system is produced, and the melting point increases to 420°C (decomp.).[57] Very high melting points are also obtained when the acetylenic group, $-C \equiv C-$, is placed in a similar position,[58] doubtless in consequence of the rigid nature and linear symmetry of the triple bond.

(c) The aromatic/hydroaromatic replacement and certain effects of conformation

It has been noted above that 1,4-cyclohexanoid rings are capable, like benzenoid, of raising the melting points of linear polyesters as compared with the acyclic analogues, and that the rings having a *trans* combination of the attached groups are more powerful in this respect than the *cis*, again for reasons of symmetry. It is of interest to compare these effects with those of benzenoid groups. Restricting the discussion to *trans*-1,4-cyclohexane rings, which have the closest resemblance to *p*-phenylene, it is found in the sebacate polyesters of hydroquinone and *trans*-quinitol, and again in the octamethylene polyesters of terephthalic and cyclohexane-1,4-dicarboxylic acids, that the hydroaromatic substances are lower melting by 20–30°C, an effect which could possibly be due to the greater thickness of the cyclohexane ring and the shell of hydrogen atoms which it presents to adjacent molecules. But when poly(*p*-xylylene terephthalate) (T_m 265°C) is compared with the all-*trans* form of its hexahydride (Fig. 1.4 (b)), the latter proves to be the higher melting by 55°C, a change which may be ascribed to the fact that whereas the unit

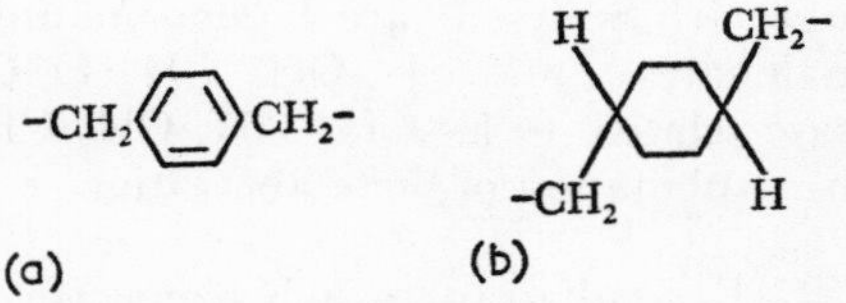

(a)   (b)

Fig. 4.4

(Fig. 4.4 (a)) lacks conformational stabilisation which would impose a fixed configuration on the ϕ—CH_2 bonds, unit (Fig. 4.4 (b)) possesses the requisite structure for such stabilisation, in the same way as occurs in the ethylenedioxy bonds of Terylene.

The flexibility of the $-O \cdot CH_2 \cdot \phi \cdot CH_2 \cdot O-$ system, and of its *m*-isomer,[59] is sustained in combination with acid units other than terephthalate.   The polyesters with alkanedioic acids, for instance, are all low-melting; but homologation to

$$-O \cdot (CH_2)_2 \cdot \phi \cdot (CH_2)_2 \cdot O-$$

again affords possibilities for conformational stabilisation in rotatory isomers of discrete energy contents, so that polyesters of these are markedly higher-melting.[10]   Of course, in higher homologues of this series the methylene dilution effect again comes into play and the influence of the ring is less marked, but the behaviour of the first members illustrates the multiplicity of factors which can result from apparently simple structural changes in polyesters.

(d)   *The replacement of chain-carbon atoms by certain other atoms*

The replacement of one atom or group of a repeating unit by another which has a substantially similar shape, and which therefore does not affect the overall configuration and symmetry of the polymer molecule, can be described as *homomorphic*.   An instance occurs when $-CH_2-$ is replaced by $-O-$.   When this replacement is effected in an open-chain situation, away from the vicinity of ring structures, there is normally a fall in melting point due to the increased ease of rotation of CH_2-O as compared with the conformationally stabilised methylene sequence; thus the compound $[-O \cdot (CH_2)_2 \cdot O \cdot (CH_2)_2 \cdot O \cdot OC \cdot \phi \cdot \phi \cdot CO-]_n$ melts at 195°C, as compared with 210–217°C for the pentamethylene homomorph,[60] and the polyesters of di- and triethylene glycols with alkanedioic acids are mainly liquids at ordinary temperatures.   This generalisation is again not without its exceptions: the polyesters of diglycollic acid (Table 4.1 Series 8) are higher-melting than the corresponding   malonates,   and $[-CH_2 \cdot CH_2 \cdot O \cdot CH_2 \cdot CO \cdot O-]_n$ shows an increase relative to $[-CH_2 \cdot CH_2 \cdot CH_2 \cdot CH_2 \cdot CO \cdot O-)_n$,[61] but no satisfying explanation of these aberrations is available at the present time.

When the $-CH_2-$ adjacent to a benzene ring is replaced by $-O-$ (compare Series 1 and 12, Table 4.1), the oxygen-homomorphs, $-\phi \cdot O \cdot (CH_2)_n \cdot O \cdot \phi-$, are higher-melting than those with the $-\phi \cdot (CH_2)_{n+2} \cdot \phi-$ unit.   This increase can be considered together with the similar one which results when polyesters containing the $-\phi \cdot CO \cdot O-$ unit are compared with the inverted $-\phi \cdot O \cdot CO-$ isomers (Fig. 4.1, Curves 2 and 3).   According to Goodman and co-workers,[9,62] the effect is due in both series to a steric impediment to rotation, present as a result of molecular geometry in the higher-melting families but not in the lower. This impediment, similar to that caused by certain *ortho*-substitutions mentioned in Section 4.2.3, is shown in Fig. 4.5 and represents a further mode of influencing the entropy of fusion of polyesters.

The substitution of —S— for —CH$_2$— in the open-chain parts of polyesters gives results similar to those mentioned for —O— in

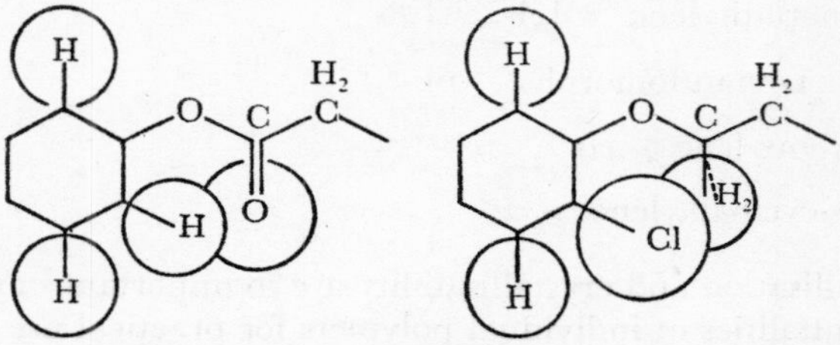

Fig. 4.5   *Illustration of types of steric hindrance possible in polyesters*

comparable situations.   Thiodivalerate polyesters of linear aliphatic diols are a little lower-melting than their methylene homomorphs, and, like the sulphonyl polymers already discussed, they suppress the normal odd-even alternation of melting points.[63]   Replacement of —CH$_2$— by —NR— cannot be classed as homomorphic, since the volume requirements of the group(s) R have a substantial effect upon the molecular shape.   Polyesters containing such units are often low melting or may even fail to crystallise.[64,65]   The groups —SiR$_2$— and —P(=O)R— in the polyester chain have similar effects, though very few comparative data are available concerning them.[66-68]   When the alcoholic —O— of the ester group is replaced by —S—, as in polythiol esters of the type

$$[—S·R·S·OC·R'·CO—]_n,$$

the melting points are higher than those of the oxygenated analogues,[69] but polythiolglycollide, $[—S·CH_2·CO—]_n$, is reported to be considerably lower melting than $[—O·CH_2·CO—]_n$ (Table 3.3 (1)).[70]

4.3   CRYSTALLISABILITY IN RELATION TO MOLECULAR STRUCTURE

Changes in the symmetry of linear polyester structures are prone to affect the ease of crystallisation in rather the same way that they affect melting points, and some of the data gathered from empirical experience can be summarised thus:

p,p'-biphenylylene $>$ p-phenylene

p-phenylene $>$ m- $>$ o-

p,p'-biphenylylene $>$ m,m'- $>$ o,o'-

2,6-naphthylene $>$ 1,4- $>$ 1,8-

D- or L-enantiomorphs $>$ DL-

trans-vinylene $>$ *cis*

trans-cycloalkylene $>$ *cis*

Crystallisation and crystallisability are so important in relation to the potentialities of individual polymers for practical use that these phenomena must be considered rather more fully in relation to molecular structure.   Unfortunately, the kinetics of crystallisation have been studied for so few polyesters that discussion can only be qualitative.

It has long been usual to assume that, provided a pattern of identically shaped and regularly placed structural units (not necessarily single chemical repeat-units) could be derived from linear polymer molecules in close and parallel packing, then crystallinity should result.   Polyesters such as those mentioned in Section 4.2.3, which for the reasons already given have their asymmetric repeat units combined in a random sequence of 'head-to-head' and 'head-to-tail' unions, fail to meet these provisos and their non-crystallinity can be explained on the basis of this lack of periodic spatial identities.   There are, however, many linear polyesters which are at least notionally regular in structure but which, in practice, crystallise only with great difficulty or not at all. Recent years have also brought the recognition of many others which are structurally irregular in the above sense but which nevertheless crystallise, sometimes with great ease.   The criteria determining whether polyesters crystallise or not are therefore no longer as capable of clear definition as once appeared.

Often the procurement of a polyester in crystalline form is a matter of method or of time.   Poly(ethylene phthalate) and poly(ethylene isophthalate) were both long regarded as uncrystallisable, although there was no convincing cause for this; but both have now been obtained in crystalline form.[24,30]   The compound

$[-OC \cdot \phi \cdot CO \cdot O \cdot (CH_2)_2 \cdot O \cdot (CH_2)_2 \cdot O-]_n$ was originally obtained as a gum, but a sample which had stood for some years in the writer's laboratory was found to have crystallised. Treatments with non-solvent liquids, by thermal annealing, precipitation from solution, perfusion with organic vapours, the evaporation of solvents from solutions of the polymers, and mechanical working are some techniques which can serve to induce crystallisation in difficult cases. Such polyesters are generally of awkward molecular shape or low symmetry where segments cannot easily adopt a regular spatial pattern: here the problem is therefore one of kinetics rather than of feasibility. Nevertheless, a residuum of polyesters of apparently regular structure has resisted all attempts at crystallisation. Examples include maleic polyesters of various symmetrical diols (Fig. 4.6 (a)) and poly(ethylene diphenyl ether 4,4'-dicarboxylate) (Fig. 4.6 (b)).

$$[-O \cdot (CH_2)_x \cdot O \cdot OC \cdot CH{=}CH \cdot CO-]_n$$
$$cis$$

(a)

$$[-O \cdot (CH_2)_2 \cdot O \cdot OC \cdot \phi \cdot O \cdot \phi \cdot CO-]_n$$

(b)

Fig. 4.6

A prerequisite for normal crystallisation is that the ordered (crystalline) phase should have a lower energy-content (i.e. a greater thermodynamic stability) than the disordered amorphous state. These polymers may therefore represent cases where the amorphous is the energetically more favoured state. In (Fig. 4.6 (b)) the central valence-angle and bond-lengths of the ϕ—O—ϕ unit are such that rotation of the benzene rings around the ϕ—O axes is strongly hindered, and the attainment of a suitable posture for lattice formation is apparently impossible. When the central —O— is replaced by —CH_2—, this hindrance is somewhat relaxed and the polyester crystallises, though with some difficulty. If, instead, the benzene rings are connected by —$(CH_2)_2$— or —SO_2—, then crystallisation occurs readily, and when the two rings are linked directly as in (Table 3.3 (11a–d)) the ease of crystallisation is so extreme that quenching to the amorphous state is impossible. The impact of molecular geometry is thus of overriding importance.

The converse case of crystallisation in irregularly constituted polyesters again proves to be determined by the balance of effects of different parts of the molecular repeat unit. Although neither poly(ethylene methylterephthalate) nor poly(1,2-propylene terephthalate) has been made to crystallise, the compounds shown in Fig. 4.7 (a–c) all do;[71] it will be noted that each of these has a lower melting point than the unsubstituted (symmetrical) analogue.

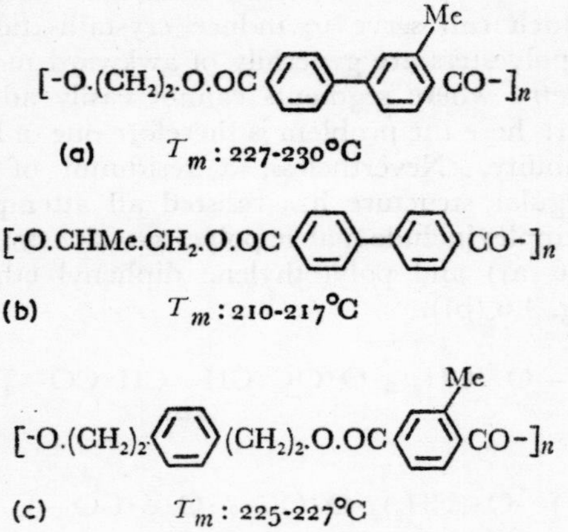

$$[-O.(CH_2)_2.O.OC \quad \bigcirc\!\!-\!\!\bigcirc^{Me} \quad CO-]_n$$

(a) T_m : 227-230°C

$$[-O.CHMe.CH_2.O.OC \quad \bigcirc\!\!-\!\!\bigcirc \quad CO-]_n$$

(b) T_m : 210-217°C

$$[-O.(CH_2)_2 \bigcirc (CH_2)_2.O.OC \quad \bigcirc^{Me} \quad CO-]_n$$

(c) T_m : 225-227°C

Fig. 4.7

The amount of compensation by symmetrical groupings needed to confer crystallisability on such polyesters depends on the degree of asymmetry present. Thus, in homologous series of the poly-(alkylene monosubstituted-terephthalates), the methylterephthalates crystallise from the tetramethylene member upwards and the bromoterephthalates, with a larger interfering group, from hexamethylene upwards—both with a hiatus at the odd-carbon member immediately following the first crystallising even member—whilst the small bulk of the fluorine atom allows all members of the fluoroterephthalate series to be crystalline.[9]

4.4 MOLECULAR CONFIGURATIONS IN THE CRYSTALLINE PHASE OF POLYESTERS

Knowledge of the positions in space occupied by the atoms of crystalline compounds affords a powerful means for the rational consideration of molecular properties, and it is therefore regrettable that the difficulties of X-ray crystallographic analysis have been resolved for so few linear polyesters. Otherwise, the molecular interpretations envisaged previously for various properties of crystalline polyesters would have a much firmer basis. Nevertheless, partial crystallographic data exist for quite a number of these compounds, and, even when these consist only of measurements of the fundamental repeating distances along the axes of oriented fibres, useful deductions can be made about the configurations of individual polymer chains, though not about their intermolecular relationships. In poly(ethylene terephthalate), for example, knowledge of the fibre identity period of 10·75 Å is sufficient to indicate the near-complete extension of the molecular chains, and hence the *trans* conformation of the ethylenedioxy groups and the opposed configuration of the ester groups of each benzene ring.

Deductions of the configurations of a considerable number of polyesters, mainly based on this type of measurement, are given in Table 4.5. Polyesters of the poly(ethylene terephthalate) type (i.e. those having no structural factors which interfere with the attainment of a fully extended configuration in which all the groupings are in the *trans* or opposed forms) appear in the upper part, and they include ring-containing as well as acyclic types. For the latter, Mnyukh[79] has shown how with increasing paraffinic character the unit cells approach increasingly closely to that of polyethylene, the structures being determined basically by the packing of the methylene groups. Parts (*b*) and (*c*) of Table 4.5 formulate polyesters which fail to attain this condition. The compounds of part (*b*) are generally only slightly distorted from full extension, by contractions of up to 3 Å in the crystal repeat-unit, and whilst accurate knowledge is lacking, it may be conjectured that this contraction occurs by limited rotations away from planarity in each segment; the polyesters of part (*c*) show such marked deviations from the simple values for full extension that they must be supposed to belong to crystallographically distinct families, possibly complex helices.

The polyesters of part (*b*) include a number mentioned earlier as having apparently abnormal melting points. Some of those listed are the odd chain-atom numbered members of homologous series, and poly(neopentylene succinate) was given above as an instance of abnormal melting point following methyl-substitution. In the case of polymers having odd numbers of chain atoms in the *chemical* repeating unit, it is necessary to have two such units in order to provide a *structural* identity period, as shown schematically in Fig. 4.8, and a number of 'abnormal' polymers are of this class. There is no reason, however, to predict abnormality of crystal structure from this fact alone. Indeed, there is a doubled chemical repeating

Table 4.5 MOLECULAR CONFIGURATIONS OF CRYSTALLINE POLYESTERS

(a) Polyesters having substantially fully extended chains	Reference

$-O \cdot (CH_2)_2 \cdot O \cdot OC \cdot (CH_2)_n \cdot CO-$ $(n = 4, 6-8)$ 72

$-O \cdot (CH_2)_9 \cdot CO-$ 72

$-O \cdot (CH_2)_{10} \cdot O \cdot OC \cdot (CH_2)_n \cdot CO-$ $(n = 0, 2, 3, 4, 6, 7, 8)$ 73

$-O \cdot (CH_2)_9 \cdot O \cdot OC \cdot (CH_2)_4 \cdot CO-$ 74

$-O \cdot (CH_2)_{20} \cdot O \cdot OC \cdot (CH_2)_{10} \cdot CO-$ 75

$-O \cdot (CH_2)_n \cdot O \cdot OC \cdot \phi \cdot CO-$ $(n = 2, 6, 8, 10)$ 8, 9

$-O \cdot (CH_2)_n \cdot \phi \cdot (CH_2)_n \cdot O \cdot OC \cdot \phi \cdot CO-$ $(2n = 4, 8, 12)$ 10

trans $-O \cdot CH_2 \langle \bigcirc \rangle CH_2 \cdot O \cdot OC \cdot \phi \cdot CO-$ 76

trans $-O \cdot CH_2 \langle \bigcirc \rangle CH_2 \cdot O \cdot OC \langle \bigcirc \rangle^R CO-$ $(R = Me, OMe)$ 71

$-O \cdot R \cdot O \cdot OC \cdot \phi \cdot O(CH_2)_4 O \cdot \phi \cdot CO-$ $(R = (CH_2)_2, trans-CH_2 \langle \bigcirc \rangle CH_2-)$ 48

trans $-O \langle \bigcirc \rangle O \cdot CO \cdot (CH_2)_4 \cdot CO-$ 77

(b) Polyesters showing marked contraction from full extension	

$-O \cdot (CH_2)_2 \cdot O \cdot OC \cdot (CH_2)_2 \cdot CO-$ 72

$-O \cdot (CH_2)_3 \cdot O \cdot OC \cdot (CH_2)_n \cdot CO-$ $(n = 2-10)$ 74

$-O \cdot (CH_2)_{10} \cdot O \cdot OC \cdot CH_2 \cdot O \cdot CH_2 \cdot CO-$ 74

$-O \cdot CH_2 \cdot CMe_2 \cdot CH_2 \cdot O \cdot OC \cdot (CH_2)_n \cdot CO-$ $(n = 4, 7, 8)$ 31

$-O \cdot (CH_2)_n \cdot O \cdot OC \cdot \phi \cdot CO-$ $(n = 3, 4, 5, 7, 9)$ 9

$-O \cdot (CH_2)_n \cdot \phi \cdot (CH_2)_n \cdot O \cdot OC \cdot \phi \cdot CO-$ $(2n = 10)$ 10

$-O \cdot (CH_2)_2 \cdot O \cdot \phi \cdot CO-$ 71

$-O \cdot (CH_2)_2 \cdot O \langle \bigcirc \rangle^{MeO} CO-$ 78

trans $-O \langle \bigcirc \rangle O \cdot OC \cdot (CH_2)_8 \cdot CO-$ 77

$-O \cdot R \cdot O \cdot OC \cdot \phi \cdot O \cdot (CH_2)_2 \cdot O \cdot \phi \cdot CO-$, $(R = (CH_2)_2, trans-CH_2 \langle \bigcirc \rangle CH_2-)$ 48

(c) Polyesters having abnormal structures	

$-O \cdot (CH_2)_3 \cdot \phi \cdot (CH_2)_3 \cdot O \cdot OC \cdot \phi \cdot CO-$

$-O \cdot CH_2 \cdot CMe_2 \cdot CH_2 \cdot O \cdot OC \cdot (CH_2)_2 \cdot CO-$ 10
     31

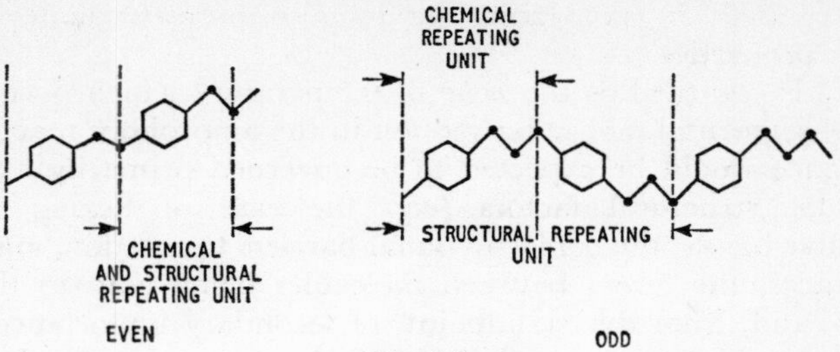

Fig. 4.8

unit in the crystallographic repeating unit of the poly(ethylene 2,5-disubstituted-terephthalates), although the molecules are fully extended in the same way as in Terylene, the doubling being suggested as due to an alternating configuration of the benzene rings,[32] shown in Fig. 4.9.

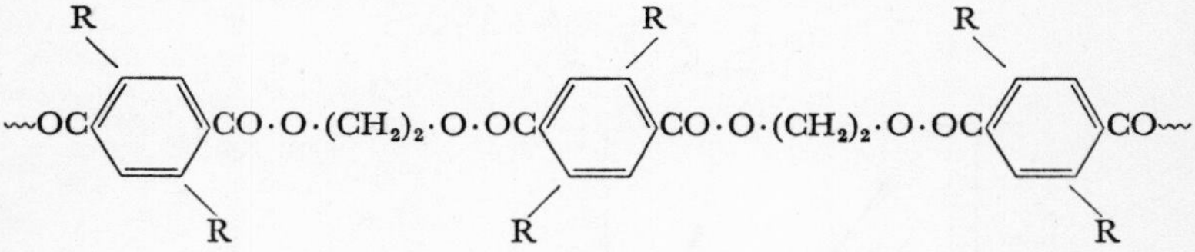

Fig. 4.9

These polyesters, incidentally, have a dilated a dimension of the unit cell (8·37 Å as compared with 4·56 Å in the simple terephthalate) which is caused by the size of the R groups. A similar expansion is noted in the lateral spacing of poly(cyclohexane-1,4-dimethylene methoxyterephthalate),[71] and in this context mention may also be made of the views propounded by Statton[80] concerning variations which are possible in the side-by-side packing of some polyester chains, where various types of rotational or longitudinal intermolecular disorder can coexist with strict periodicity along each molecular chain.

4.5 GLASS-RUBBER TRANSITION TEMPERATURES

The glass-rubber transition temperature T_g is a property of the amorphous state of polymers. It is important in connection with the conditions in which crystallisation or orientation can be brought about, as well as for the behaviour of certain mechanical properties of polymers in relation to temperature (see Sections 3.2–3.4). Knowledge of the way in which T_g depends upon structure is therefore useful in considering the design of polyester molecules for specific properties.

If T_g is regarded as the zone of temperature which permits the onset of segmental molecular motion in the amorphous material, its occurrence would be expected to be governed primarily by intra-molecular structural factors (e.g. the ease of flexing around particular bonds, the conformational barriers to rotation, and steric hindrance), the forces between molecules being akin to those in liquids, and, from this standpoint, of secondary importance. For polyesters which are essentially bonded by van der Waals forces, this assumption appears to be justified, and since the background to the intramolecular factors which govern molecular mobility has already been discussed in connection with the melting points, the structural dependence of T_g can be summarised quite shortly.

As a general rule, the aliphatic polyesters of all-linear structure

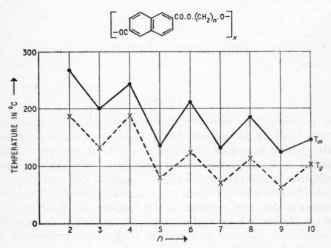

Fig. 4.10   Melting and glass-transition temperatures of poly(alkylene naphthalene-2,6-dicarboxylates)

have glass-transition temperatures well below room temperature, mainly in the range $-70°C$ to $-20°C$; ring-containing polyesters which also have a substantial acyclic-chain content have T_g's falling in the range $20°C$ to $150°C$, and where the proportion of rings is higher, the T_g's increase up to a maximum of about $250-280°C$, which is found in such materials as poly(p-phenylene terephthalate); Table 3.3 gives the glass-transition temperatures of a number of polyesters. From Fig. 4.10 which displays the changes in both T_g and T_m with increasing methylene content in the poly-(alkylene naphthalene-2,6-dicarboxylates),[81] it will be seen that both properties are sensitive to structure, and the data in Table 3.3 also show how the high-melting aliphatic polyesters have correspondingly high T_g's.

Edgar[82] noted that, when T_m and T_g were expressed in °K, then both for poly(ethylene terephthalate) and poly(ethylene adipate), $T_m \simeq 1\cdot7\ T_g$, and some writers have assumed subsequently that this relationship is generally valid. This is not so, however, as may be seen when poly(ethylene terephthalate) is compared with the crystalline but lower-melting 2,5-dimethyl or 2,5-dichloroterephthalates and with the amorphous methyl-, chloro-, or bromoterephthalates. All of these compounds, having similar molecular skeleta, enter the glass transition in about the same range of temperature, namely 80–110°C, there being some margin of variance with crystallinity; the same is true for a variety of other substituted polyesters in comparison with their parents. Features of the molecular backbone which determine the melting point are thus likely to have effects in the same sense on the T_g but there is no reason to expect a precise correspondence between the two.

4.6 HYDROLYTIC AND THERMAL STABILITY

The chemical behaviour of polymers generally is characteristic of their constituent structural features rather than of the macromolecular state. Each component plays its own role in relation to the chemical reactivity of the material as, for example, in the double-bond reactivity of the unsaturated polyesters, which is independent of the polyester group to which the substances belong. The hydrolytic behaviour which is to be discussed is, of course, inherent in the esters as a class, and the notes which follow on thermal stability will deal only with those aspects where the ester-character is involved.

The susceptibilities of polyesters of different structural types towards hydrolysis can vary very greatly, some being stable to all but the most vigorous conditions of attack, and others being labile to the point of inutility. Owing to the solid character and heterogeneous texture of most practical polymers, accurate physicochemical kinetic data concerning their reactivities are less easily accessible than for simple substances, and the comparison of different polymers mainly depends upon empirical observations of behaviour in practical but sometimes arbitrary conditions. It is therefore satisfying that the observed order of hydrolytic stabilities, in which the polyesters of dihydric phenols rank lower than linear aliphatic polyesters which, in turn, are less resistant than those of the aliphatic alcohol/aromatic acid type, conforms with the known decreasing tendency of these ester types, as simple compounds, to undergo hydrolysis with water alone or in conditions of acid or alkaline catalysis. Therefore, when significant differences in reactivity are shown up in the empirical testing of more varied types of structures, it is likely that they do reflect underlying molecular realities. The comparisons in Fig. 4.11, which are derived from a number of patent specifications, show such differences in the ease of hydrolysis of the polyesters whose repeat-units are shown, the compounds on the right in each line thus being the most stable.

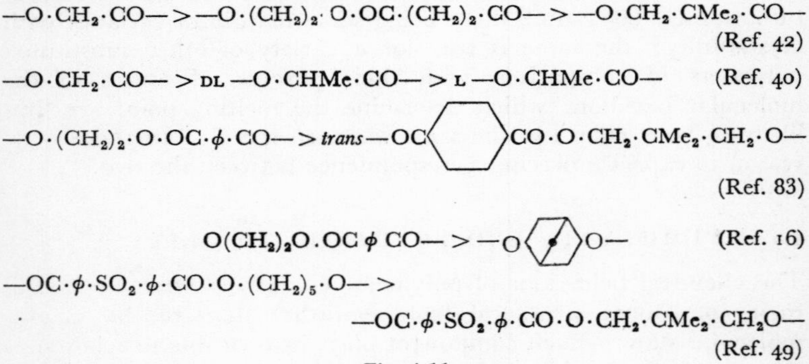

$$-O \cdot CH_2 \cdot CO- > -O \cdot (CH_2)_2 \cdot O \cdot OC \cdot (CH_2)_2 \cdot CO- > -O \cdot CH_2 \cdot CMe_2 \cdot CO-$$

(Ref. 42)

$$-O \cdot CH_2 \cdot CO- > \text{DL} -O \cdot CHMe \cdot CO- > \text{L} -O \cdot CHMe \cdot CO-$$ (Ref. 40)

$$-O \cdot (CH_2)_2 \cdot O \cdot OC \cdot \phi \cdot CO- > trans - OC \langle \bigcirc \rangle CO \cdot O \cdot CH_2 \cdot CMe_2 \cdot CH_2 \cdot O-$$

(Ref. 83)

$$O(CH_2)_2 O \cdot OC \, \phi \, CO- > -O \langle \bigcirc \rangle O-$$ (Ref. 16)

$$-OC \cdot \phi \cdot SO_2 \cdot \phi \cdot CO \cdot O \cdot (CH_2)_5 \cdot O- >$$

$$-OC \cdot \phi \cdot SO_2 \cdot \phi \cdot CO \cdot O \cdot CH_2 \cdot CMe_2 \cdot CH_2O-$$

(Ref. 49)

Fig. 4.11

Owing to differences between the various groups in the test methods used and in the physical forms of the samples, direct inter-group comparison is not possible, but there appears a general indication that the presence of methyl groups as side-chains in the proximity of the ester linkages affords a greater stability towards hydrolysis. Explanation of this must again be tentative. One possibility is that these groups simply impede the access of molecules of the hydrolytic agent to the ester groups. Another is that the hindrance to chain-rotation caused by these groups makes it less facile for the amorphous regions of the polymer to attain reactive configurations. Huisgen and Ott[84] have shown that, of two possible configurations shown below for the ester group in simple lactones, the former (*cis*-configuration) is far more readily hydrolysed; and it is plausible that polyesters where the amorphous regions can more readily produce this form might be the more labile. (See Fig. 4.12).

Various aspects of the thermal stability of polyesters have already been mentioned in connection with general methods for the synthesis of these compounds (Sections **2.2**, **2.3**, and **2.5**) and with the molecular behaviour of poly(ethylene terephthalate) (Section **3.2**). The topic is of greater concern to the research worker and to

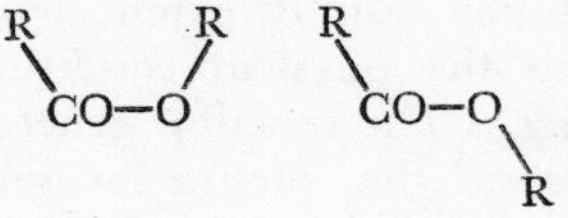

$$
\begin{array}{ccc}
\text{R} & \text{R} \quad \text{R} \\
\diagdown & \diagup \quad \diagdown \\
\text{CO—O} & \text{CO—O} \\
& \diagdown \\
& \text{R}
\end{array}
$$

cis   *trans*

Fig. 4.12

the polyester manufacturer than to the plastics or fibre technologist, since no polyester which is thermally unstable in its intended conditions of fabrication or use is likely to be released commercially; but the patterns of thermal reactions of polyesters are worthy of discussion.

The important thermal decomposition reactions of linear polyesters are (i) depolymerisation, and (ii) scission of ester groups to carboxylic acid and olefine

$$(\sim\!\!CO\cdot O\cdot CH_2\cdot CH_2\!\!\sim \longrightarrow \sim\!\!CO_2H + CH_2\!:\!CH\!\!\sim);$$

and these reactions may occur concurrently, although at different rates. Since bulk samples of polyesters normally contain residues of the catalysts of the polycondensation reaction, it is possible for these to assist decomposition reactions at high temperatures, but the reactions under consideration are inherent in the nature of the polymers, so that at most such residues will only affect their extents.

The depolymerisation reaction, forming low-molecular cyclic esters, is a natural result of probabilities arising from the interchange which normally occurs between ester groups in polyesters at high temperatures. The normal reaction can be expressed as shown in Fig. 4.13:

$$
\begin{array}{ccc}
\text{R—CO—O—R}' & & \text{R—CO—O—R}'' \\
+ & \rightleftharpoons & + \\
\text{R}''\text{—O—OC—R}''' & & \text{R}'\text{—O—OC—R}'''
\end{array}
$$

Fig. 4.13

and the variant leading to depolymerisation can occur by 'loop' formation in the polyester structure in Fig. 4.14:

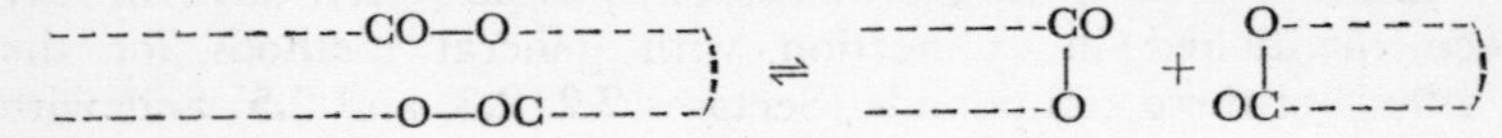

Fig. 4.14

This is a reversible reaction (compare the formation of polymers by polymerisation of lactones), and its extent depends upon the nature of the substances and the physical conditions prevailing at the temperature of heating.   The reaction generally occurs at a lower temperature than does the olefine-forming scission reaction. Aliphatic polycarbonates and other aliphatic polyesters can be converted in substantial degree to cyclic mono- or dilactones (the structures of the products depending on the sizes of the methylene sequences in the polyesters) by heating to above 200°C in high vacua so that the volatile products are removed continuously as formed.[85]   A similar cyclisation occurs with linear poly(ethylene terephthalate) at temperatures above the melting point, but here the cyclic products are involatile and are formed only to the small proportion permitted by the equilibrium between straight-chain and ring forms;[86] poly(ethylene isophthalate) also depolymerises, though with greater ease, giving a cyclic dimeric ester.[89]

The olefine-forming reaction normally becomes prominent only at temperatures approaching 300°C and is a slower process, although in a few instances where conjugation in the product plays a special part (the breakdown of tetramethylene polyesters to butadiene, of phenylenediethyl esters to divinylbenzene, and of ethylene-2-carboxylates to acrylic acids) it may be unusually facile.   Once the primary scission has occurred, further reactions of considerable complexity may follow, as already exemplified for poly(ethylene terephthalate).

It will be seen that the olefine-forming reaction can only take place when a hydrogen atom is attached to the chain-carbon atom second to the ester linkage at the 'alcohol' side.   When this is not present, as in the neopentylene polyesters containing the group —O·CH$_2$·CR$_2$·CH$_2$·O—, an enhanced thermal stability can be expected, and some evidence supporting this view was provided by Pohl.[87]

There remain some rather specific thermal decomposition reactions which are not obviously classifiable with the foregoing cases, and in which carbon dioxide forms a characteristic reaction

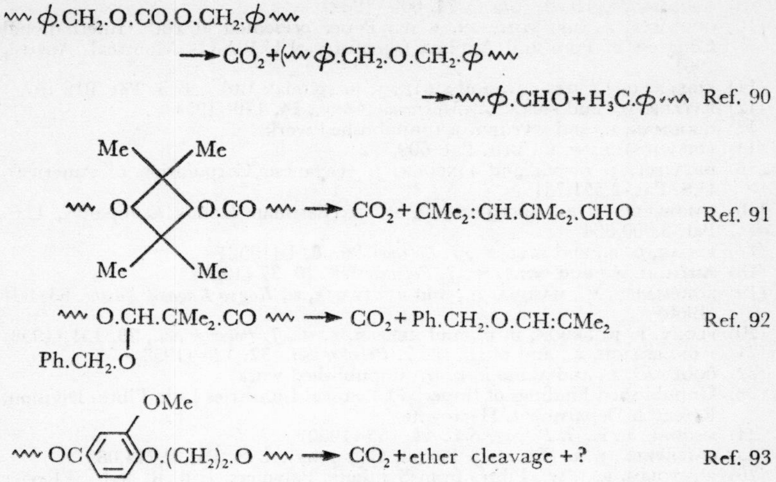

$\sim\sim \phi.CH_2.O.CO.O.CH_2.\phi\sim\sim$

$\longrightarrow CO_2+\{\sim\sim\phi.CH_2.O.CH_2.\phi\sim\sim$

$\longrightarrow\sim\sim\phi.CHO+H_3C.\phi\sim\sim$ Ref. 90

$\sim\sim O\diagdown\diagup O.CO \sim\sim \longrightarrow CO_2+CMe_2:CH.CMe_2.CHO$ Ref. 91

(with Me, Me substituents above and below the central carbons)

$\sim\sim O.CH.CMe_2.CO \sim\sim \longrightarrow CO_2+Ph.CH_2.O.CH:CMe_2$ Ref. 92
$\quad\quad |$
$Ph.CH_2.O$

$\sim\sim OC\langle\!\!\!\!\bigcirc\!\!\!\!\rangle O.(CH_2)_2.O \sim\sim \longrightarrow CO_2+ether\ cleavage+?$ Ref. 93
(with OMe substituent on the ring)

Fig. 4.15

product. Carothers and Van Natta[88] observed a reaction of this sort with poly(trimethylene carbonate) which, as low as 210°C, broke down thus:

$$[-O\cdot(CH_2)_3\cdot O\cdot CO-]_n \longrightarrow n\ HO\cdot CH_2\cdot CH:CH_2 + n\ CO_2$$

Other polyesters giving somewhat similar reactions, though not necessarily by the same mechanism, include those in Fig. 4.15.

REFERENCES

(1) KORSHAK, V. V., and VINOGRADOVA, S. V., *Izvest. Akad. Nauk S.S.S.R., Otdel. Khim. Nauk*, 148 (1959)
(2) ZAHN, H., RATHGEBER, P., REXROTH, E., KRZIKALLA, R., LAUER, W., MIRÓ, P., SPOOR, H., SCHMIDT, F., SEIDEL, B., and HILDEBRAND, D., *Angew. Chem.*, **68**, 229 (1956)
(3) ZAHN, H., and KRZIKALLA, R., *Makromol. Chem.*, **23**, 31 (1957)
(4) ZAHN, H., and SEIDEL, B., *Makromol. Chem.*, **29**, 70 (1959)
(5) CAROTHERS, W. H., and VAN NATTA, F. J., *J. Amer. Chem. Soc.*, **55**, 4714 (1933)
(6) BATZER, H., and LANG, H., *Makromol. Chem.*, **15**, 211 (1955)
(7) BATZER, H., and MOHR, B., *Makromol. Chem.*, **8**, 217 (1952)
(8) DAUBENY, R. DE P., BUNN, C. W., and BROWN, C. J., *Proc. Roy. Soc.*, **A226**, 531 (1954)

112   *Polyesters*

(9) GOODMAN, I., *Angew. Chem.*, **74**, 606 (1962)

(10) GOODMAN, I., and STIMPSON, J. W., Paper presented at 18th. International Congress of Pure and Applied Chemistry, I.U.P.A.C., Montreal, August, 1961

(11) KIBLER, C. J., BELL, A., and SMITH, J. G. (Kodak Ltd.), Brit. Pat. 818,157

(12) BATZER, H., and FRITZ, G., *Makromol. Chem.*, **14**, 179 (1954)

(13) GOODMAN, I., and MATHER, J. (unpublished work)

(14) BIRTWHISTLE, W. K., Brit. Pat. 609,792

(15) DREWITT, J. G. N., and LINCOLN, J. (Celanese Corporation of America), U.S. Pat. 2,551,731

(16) CALDWELL, J. R., and JACKSON, W. J. (Eastman Kodak Company), U.S. Pat. 3,000,864

(17) EDGAR, O. B., and HILL, R., *J. Polymer Sci.*, **8**, 1 (1952)

(18) SMITH, C. W., and DOLE, M., *J. Polymer Sci.*, **20**, 37 (1956)

(19) KOREMATSU, M., MASUDA, H., and KURIYAMA, S., *Kogyo Kagaku Zasshi*, **63**, 884 (1960)

(20) FLORY, P. J., BEDON, H. D., and KEEFER, E. H., *J. Polymer Sci.*, **28**, 151 (1958)

(21) WUNDERLICH, B., and DOLE, M., *J. Polymer Sci.*, **32**, 125 (1958)

(22) GOODMAN, I., and ALDRED, D. H. (unpublished work)

(23) Unpublished Findings of Imperial Chemical Industries Ltd., Fibres Division, Research Department, Harrogate

(24) FISCHER, R. F., *J. Polymer Sci.*, **44**, 155 (1960)

(25) CALDWELL, J. R. (Eastman Kodak Company), U.S. Pat. 2,744,089

(26) REYNOLDS, R. J. W., Fibres from Synthetic Polymers, Hill, R. (ed.), Elsevier Publishing Company, Chap. 6 (1953)

(27) CALDWELL, J. R. (Eastman Kodak Company), U.S. Pat. 2,744,129

(28) MARTIN, E. V., *Textile Res. J.*, **32**, 619 (1962)

(29) MARVEL, C. S., and YOUNG, C. H., *J. Amer. Chem. Soc.*, **73**, 1066 (1951)

(30) CONIX, A., and VAN KERPEL, R., *J. Polymer Sci.*, **40**, 521 (1959)

(31) DOAK, K. W., and CAMPBELL, H. N., *J. Polymer Sci.*, **18**, 215 (1955)

(32) CACHIA, M., *Ann. Chim.*, **4**, 5 (1959)

(33) Edogawa Chemical Co. Ltd., Japanese Pat. 13799/62

(34) LINCOLN, J. (British Celanese Limited), U.S. Pats. 2,692,248–9

(35) GOODMAN, I., and STIMPSON, J. W. (unpublished results)

(36) CALDWELL, J. R., and GILKEY, R. (Eastman Kodak Company), U.S. Pat. 3,053,805

(37) WHEELER, D. D. (The Dow Chemical Company), U.S. Pat. 3,054,779

(38) KORSHAK, V. V., and VINOGRADOVA, S. V., *Izvest. Akad. Nauk S.S.S.R., Otdel. Khim. Nauk*, 154 (1959)

(39) Esso Research and Engineering Company, British Pat. 790,505

(40) SALZBERG, P. L. (E. I. du Pont de Nemours and Co.), U.S. Pat. 2,758,987

(41) KLEINE, J., and KLEINE, H.-H., *Makromol. Chem.*, **30**, 23 (1959)

(42) ALDERSON, T. (E. I. du Pont de Nemours and Co.), U.S. Pat. 2,658,055

(43) REYNOLDS, R. J. W., and VICKERS, E. J. (Imperial Chemical Industries Ltd.), British Pat. 766,347

(44) VICKERS, E. J., and REYNOLDS, R. J. W. (Imperial Chemical Industries Ltd.), British Pat. 775,495

(45) ÉTIENNE, Y. P. M., and FISCHER, N. (Kodak-Pathé), French Pat. 1,231,163

(46) NATTA, G., MAZZANTI, G., PREGAGLIA, G., and BINAGHI, M. (Montecatini Società Generale per L'Industria Mineraria e Chimica), Belgian Pat. 600,910

(47) OKAMURA, S., HAYASHI, K., and KITANISHI, Y., *J. Polymer Sci.*, **58**, 925 (1962)

(48) Unpublished Observations of the Research Department, Imperial Chemical Industries Ltd., Fibres Division, Harrogate

(49) CALDWELL, J. R., and WELLMAN, J. W. (Eastman Kodak Company), U.S. Pat. 2,921,052

(50) GORDON, D. A. (The Dow Chemical Company), U.S. Pat. 3,047,536

(51) HAGEMEYER, H. J. (Eastman Kodak Company), U.S. Pat. 3,043,808

(52) SCHWEIKER, G. C., and ROBITSCHEK, P., *J. Polymer Sci.*, **24**, 33 (1957) idem (Hooker Chemical Corporation), U.S. Pat. 3,016,360
(53) Dow Corning Corporation, Brit. Pat. 798,824
(54) OTTMAN, G. F. (Olin Mathieson Chemical Corporation), U.S. Pat. 3,044,988
(55) GLEIM, W. K. T. (Universal Oil Products Co.), U.S. Pat. 3,039,994
(56) SMITH, W. M., EBERLEY, K. C., HANSON, E. O., and BINDER, J. L., *J. Amer. Chem. Soc.*, **78**, 626 (1956)
(57) California Research Corporation, Brit. Pat. 693,375
(58) LAAKSO, T. M., and REYNOLDS, D. D. (Eastman Kodak Company), U.S. Pat. 2,856,384
(59) KORSHAK, V. V., and VINOGRADOVA, S. V., *Izvest. Akad. Nauk S.S.S.R., Otdel. Khim. Nauk*, 154, 338 (1959)
(60) GOODMAN, I., and MILBURN, A. H. (unpublished work)
(61) SCHULTZ, H. S. (General Aniline & Film Corporation), U.S. Pats. 3,063,967–8
(62) GOODMAN, I., MATHER, J., and STIMPSON, J. W., Paper presented at International Symposium on Macromolecular Chemistry, I.U.P.A.C., Montreal, 1961
(63) KORSHAK, V. V., and VINOGRADOVA, S. V., *J. Gen. Chem.* (Moscow), **26**, 732 (1956)
(64) WHINFIELD, J. R., and BIRTWHISTLE, W. K., Brit. Pat. 572, 671
(65) ANDRES, R. J. (E. I. du Pont de Nemours and Company), U.S. Pat. 3,065,207
(66) SOMMER, L. H. (Dow Corning Corporation), U.S. Pat. 2,963,500
(67) KORSHAK, V. V., *J. Polymer Sci.*, **31**, 319 (1958)
(68) MORGAN, P. W. (E. I. du Pont de Nemours and Company), U.S. Pat. 2,646,420
(69) MURPHEY, W. A. (E. I. du Pont de Nemours and Company), U.S. Pat. 2,870,126
(70) SCHÖBERL, A., Paper presented at International Symposium on Macromolecules, I.U.P.A.C., Wiesbaden, 1959
(71) GOODMAN, I., MILBURN, A. H., MCINTYRE, J. E., and STIMPSON, J. W. (unpublished work)
(72) FULLER, C. S., and FROSCH, C. J., *J. Phys. Chem.*, **43**, 323 (1939)
(73) FULLER, C. S., and FROSCH, C. J., *J. Amer. Chem. Soc.*, **61**, 2575 (1939)
(74) FULLER, C. S., FROSCH, C. J., and PAPE, N. R., *J. Amer. Chem. Soc.*, **64**, 154 (1942)
(75) MNYUKH, YU. M., *J. Phys. Chem.* (Moscow), **33**, 2190 (1959)
(76) BOYE, C. A., *J. Polymer Sci.*, **55**, 263, 275 (1961)
(77) TAKAHASHI, M., *Sen-I-Gakkaishi*, **14**, 374 (1958) (through *Chem. Abstr.*, **52**, 21217 (1958))
(78) KOREMATSU, M., and KURIYAMA, S., *Nippon Kagaku Zasshi*, **81**, 852 (1960) (through *Chem. Abstr.*, **55**, 12991 (1961))
(79) MNYUKH, YU. M., *Izvest. Akad. Nauk S.S.S.R., Otdel. Khim. Nauk*, 1128 (1958)
(80) STATTON, W. O., *Ann. N.Y. Acad. Sci.*, **83**, 27 (1959)
(81) GOODMAN, I., MARSDEN, R. J. B., and MILBURN, A. H. (unpublished work)
(82) EDGAR, O. B., *J. Chem. Soc.*, 2638 (1952)
(83) CALDWELL, J. R., and GILKEY, R. (Eastman Kodak Company), U.S. Pat. 2,891,930
(84) HUISGEN, R., and OTT, H., *Tetrahedron*, **6**, 253 (1959)
(85) Collected Papers of Wallace Hume Carothers (Mark, H., and Whitby, G. S., Eds.), Interscience Publishers Inc., New York (1940)
(86) GOODMAN, I., and NESBITT, B. F., *J. Polymer Sci.*, **47**, 423 (1960)
(87) POHL, H. A., *J. Amer. Chem. Soc.*, **73**, 5660 (1951)
(88) CAROTHERS, W. H., and VAN NATTA, F. J., *J. Amer. Chem. Soc.*, **52**, 314 (1930)
(89) BERR, C. E., *J. Polymer Sci.*, **15**, 591 (1955)
(90) REYNOLDS, D. D., and VAN DEN BERGHE, J. (Eastman Kodak Company) U.S. Pat. 2,789,509
(91) GAWLAK, M., PALMER, R. P., ROSE, J. B. SANDIFORD, D. J. H., and TURNER-JONES, A., *Chem. & Ind.*, 1148 (1962)
(92) MILLER, R. G. J., NIELD, E., and TURNER-JONES, A., *Chem. & Ind.*, 181 (1962)
(93) MURAKAMI, K., and TACHI, I., *Nippon Mokuzai Gakkaish*, **6**, 16 (1960) (Through *Chem. Abstr.*, **54**, 25951 (1960))

CHAPTER 5

COPOLYESTERS, MODIFIED POLYESTERS, AND RELATED COMPOUNDS

5.1 INTRODUCTION

Many of the methods available for the synthesis of polyesters can be adapted to the formation of copolyesters—substances containing more than one type of structural building unit in their molecular chains—and the number of such compounds which have been described is very large.

The normal polyester-forming reactions, when applied to mixtures of more than one type of hydroxy-acid, dicarboxylic acid, or diol, are not conducive to the combination of the residues of the reactants in any special sequence. Moreover, the ester-ester interchange reactions, which are a feature of the chemical behaviour of polyesters at the temperatures usually required for synthesis by polycondensation, would assure that copolyesters formed from a multiplicity of reactants will have their component groups linked in a random (statistical) order. The majority of known copolyesters is of this type, and a binary copolyester composed of the units A and B in the molar ratio 1:4 might therefore have a chain structure such as

—BBABAABBBBBABBBBBABBBBBBB—

In general there is no limitation except that of chemical stability on the nature, number, and proportions of polyester-forming materials which can be copolymerised, although, as already stated, when one of these is readily volatile it may be difficult to ensure that its proportion in the final product is the same as in the mixture of starting materials.

By the use of special synthetic methods it is possible in some cases to obtain copolyesters having ordered arrangements of the constituent groups. One such type is that wherein the units alternate regularly, e.g. —ABAB...ABAB—; another has more extensive sequences of all—A and all—B units combined linearly, thus:

—AAA...AA—BBBB....BBB—AAA....AA—BBB...B—

The latter are known as 'block' copolyesters, and they may have both the A and B polymeric units as members of the polyester class, or one species (say the BB...BB blocks), may be of a different chemical type (such as polyethers or polyurethanes) combined with the ester blocks —A...A— either through ester linkages or other types of bonds. Strictly, complex polyesters of the latter type are random copolymers of the B species in the polyester made of A, but to classify them in this way is to obscure a significant structural relationship.

Yet another type of copolyester has some of the hydrogen atoms attached to the basic skeleton of the polyester replaced by polymeric chains, usually of a non-polyester species. Such materials are called 'graft' copolyesters and can be represented as in Fig. 5.1, where the A's are the normal polyester repeating units.

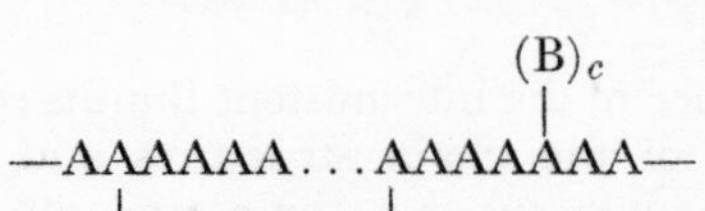

$$(B)_c$$
$$|$$
—AAAAAA...AAAAAAA—
$$|\qquad\qquad|$$
$$(B)_a\qquad\quad (B)_b$$

Fig. 5.1

Compared with the results of incorporating additive materials into polymers, as is commonly done with plasticisers, pigments, and stabilisers, copolymerisation is of an enduring character, so that any novel quality conferred by this means is preserved throughout the whole life of the material. The properties of copolyesters, which depend upon the molecular geometrical and chemical structures of their component parts and upon their relative proportions, can be varied greatly from those of the parent polyesters, and many proposals have been made for the utilisation of this principle to give polyesters of modified properties.   In recent years copolymerisation in the polyester series has proved of interest mainly in connection with the dyeing and surface properties of fibres and in the production of new types of elastomeric materials, but advances into other areas of utility may well be seen in the future.   In the following Sections the properties of the various types of copolyesters are considered in more detail.

Polyester properties can be modified by various chemical treatments other than copolymerisation; these will also be discussed, and finally a brief account will be given of polyester amides, polyphosphonic and related esters, and polysulphonic esters, which although of restricted technical importance, are nevertheless cognate to the main matter of this book.

5.2   RANDOM COPOLYESTERS

The most distinctive feature of the properties of random copolyesters can be understood by visualising the results of aligning a number of such polymer chains, each possessing the same proportions of constituent units but having them linked—as would occur in practice—in a different order (Fig. 5.2):

—BAAAAAABAAABAAA—
—AABAAAAAAABAABA—
—AAAABABAAAAABAA—
—ABAAABAAAABAAAA—

Fig. 5.2

Since the presence of the intermittent B units represents a caesura in the regularity of the chain structures and of the interchain relationships, it is apparent that the association of A units (where these are in the majority and where all-A polymer is normally crystallisable) will be impeded, and that this impedance will be the more marked the higher the proportion of B units copolymerised with A.   Difficulties will thus be caused in the crystallisation of the A's; conversely, when the B units form the major part of the structure, then the A's will interfere with their crystallisation, assuming this to be possible.   For binary copolyesters made of two species each crystallisable as a homopolymer, it is therefore usual to find a region of composition in which the ease of crystallisation is reduced; in some cases it may even be impossible to crystallise copolyesters over a certain range of composition, as in the copoly-(ethylene/*p*-xylylene terephthalates) which are amorphous when the aliphatic grouping comprises 30–70 moles % of the diol-based units present,[1] and in the copoly(2-methyltrimethylene/2,2-dimethyltrimethylene succinates) with 30–60 moles % of the first-named component.[2]

When a crystallising polyester species is copolymerised with one which is non-crystallising, then, at above some critical proportion of the latter, the copolymers are entirely amorphous. Examples are

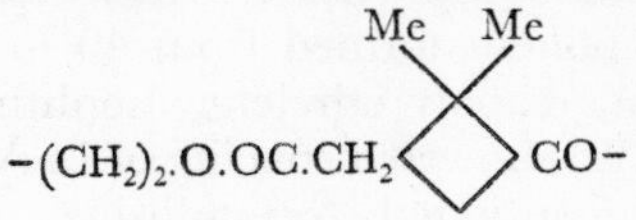

$$-(CH_2)_2.O.OC.CH_2 \underset{\diagdown}{\diagup} \overset{Me \quad Me}{\diagup \diagdown} CO-$$

Fig. 5.3

given by Wielicki and co-workers[3] for copolyesters of ethylene terephthalate (Fig. 1.4 (a)) or ethylene biphenyl-4,4'-dicarboxylate (Table 3.3 (11a)) with ethylene pinate (Fig. 5.3) which, at molar proportions exceeding 50% and 60% in the two cases, respectively, are obtained only as gummy or glassy materials. If both components of a binary copolyester are amorphous or difficultly crystallising substances, then the whole range of products will have an amorphous character.

In a small number of copolyesters which are highly crystalline over the whole range of compositions, it may be found that the combined species possess closely similar molecular unit geometries. This has been noted in some cases where the units A and B are stereoisomeric, as in the polyterephthalate of the mixed *cis/trans*-cyclohexane-1,4-dimethanols (Fig. 1.4 (b));[4] mixed crystals, possibly with the appearance of a new type of crystalline phase in the central part of the composition range, may be formed in such series. Mixed-crystal formation has also been reported for a ternary copolyester of the C_{10}, C_{11}, and C_{12} alkanedioic acids with ethylene glycol, where it may be that the $(CH_2)_n$ components so preponderate that crystallisation is mainly of the paraffinic type with local longitudinal adjustments to accommodate the occasionally displaced dipoles.[5]

The most common type of crystallinity in copolyesters is that in which the characteristic X-ray diffraction pattern of the major component is given at each end of the composition range, with increasing amorphous scatter and possibly a grossly distorted pattern as the amounts of the components become more nearly equal. Edgar and Ellery[6] found that, for bulk samples of copoly-(ethylene terephthalate/sebacate), the poly(ethylene terephthalate) powder-diffraction pattern was given at proportions down to 63 moles % of this constituent, and that the poly(ethylene sebacate) pattern was clearly defined when this ingredient formed up to 30 moles % of the whole material.   Goodman and Milburn,[7] working with oriented fibre samples, observed that a crystal spacing of 10·3 Å, possibly due to a distorted form of the ethylene terephthalate units, was present in X-ray diffraction photographs of copoly-(ethylene   terephthalate/biphenyl-4,4'-dicarboxylate)   when   the first-mentioned component formed from 40 to 60 moles % of the whole; in contrast, copoly(ethylene isophthalate/biphenyl-4,4'-dicarboxylate) (50:50) showed a spacing of 15 Å which was ascribed solely to the last mentioned (crystallising) component.   Thus, except where mixed crystal formation occurs, it is valid to con-clude that crystalline copolyesters show the crystalline character-istics of one component only, and that, particularly at low molar proportions, the 'foreign' components are accommodated entirely in the amorphous regions.

The interference of copolymeric entities with crystallisation is thus primarily with the size and perfection of the crystallites. Golike and Cobbs[8] have studied the kinetics of crystallisation of ethylene terephthalate copolymers with 5 and 10 moles % of 3-oxapentamethylene units where it was found that the rate of crystallisation was increased, relative to the homopolymer, at low temperatures but diminished at higher.

Except where mixed-crystal formation occurs, in which case the melting points of the copolyesters change monotonically with composition between those of the respective homopolymers, the effect of incorporating foreign units B into the chains of a polyester $(A)_n$ is to give products of reduced melting points.   Since the same occurs when A units are introduced into $(B)_n$, again assuming both terminal species to be crystalline, a graph of the melting points of binary copolyesters in relation to composition gives a V or U-shaped (eutectic-type) curve, the position of the bottom of the trough (i.e. the minimum melting point for the particular series) being more or less displaced from equimolarity according to the disparity between the melting points of the separate homopolymers.   A well-defined example is given in Fig. 5.4 where the terminal homopolyesters—both readily crystallising—are rather similar in melting points, and the minimum comes fairly near to the equivalent proportion of components.   Korshak and co-workers give data for tetramethylene binary copolyesters of terephthalic acid with numerous alkane-dioic acid residues, and for mixed alkanedioates, where the minima usually occur when about 20–30 moles % of the lower-melting species are present.[9]

According to Flory,[10] the melting point T_m of a random copolymer made of a minor proportion of B units in $(A)_n$, where the latter is the crystallising species, is given by:

$$\frac{1}{T_m} - \frac{1}{T_m{}^0} = -\left\{\frac{R}{\Delta H_u}\right\} \ln \mathcal{N}_A$$

where $T_m{}^0$ is the melting point of the homopolymer of A

$\mathcal{N}_A$ is the molar fraction of A units in the copolymer

ΔH_u is the heat of fusion per repeating unit of A

R is the gas constant,

There is experimental evidence[6] that the linear relationship thereby implied between composition and melting point at equilibrium crystallinity is obeyed up to a degree of modification of 30% in copolyesters of ethylene terephthalate. The molar compositions of copolyesters, such as result, for instance, from ether-forming side reactions in polycondensation, can therefore be determined from the melting points,[11] and the above equation also provides the basis of a method for the evaluation of the heats of fusion of polyesters.[12–15] The reasoning applies also to ternary or more complex copolyesters, provided that these are of random structure and that the degree of copolymerisation is not greater than the range of linear dependence.

Since the effect of copolymerisation upon melting point is measured by the *molar* and not by the *weight* fraction of the 'foreign' ingredient, the molecular weight of the latter is an important determinant of the depression which will be caused. For molecularly complex components, therefore, a higher weight-fraction can be tolerated for a given reduction in T_m than for simpler groups, a conclusion which is important in connection with the properties of block copolyesters.

There are insufficient data to allow the formulation of clear-cut generalisations about the effects of copolymerisation upon glass-transition temperatures. It would be reasonable to expect that the introduction of a more flexible entity into molecules of the amorphous parts of a copolymer would tend to lower the temperature at which molecular motion is possible, and conversely for units of greater stiffness. Where, in binary copolyesters, both combined species have somewhat similar T_g's, the glass-transition temperatures will show little change with composition (except insofar as the reduction of crystallinity may somewhat lower the values). The copolyesters of Fig. 5.4, which are of this class, all enter the glass-transition at temperatures between 90° and 100°C, whereas copolymers of ethylene terephthalate with alkanedioates do so at progressively lower temperatures as the content of aliphatic chains is increased.[16]

The consequences of the interference with crystallinity and the other general effects of copolymerisation in polyesters are so varied,

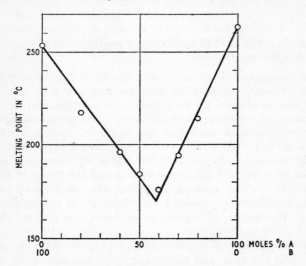

Fig. 5.4   Melting point v. composition curve for copolyesters of (A) ethylene terephthalate with (B) ethylene 1,2-diphenoxy-ethane-4,4-dicarboxylate

according to the structures concerned, that only an outline, based on a selection of indicative examples, can be given of the technically significant properties of copolyesters.   In general terms, the properties of copolyesters represent a compromise between those of the relevant homopolyesters rather than an addition of the two.   Even when a component is introduced because of possession of some unique characteristic, this will show in the final product only at the expense of some part of the main constituent qualities, but in many cases the value of copolymerisation is held to lie precisely in the mitigation of the more extreme properties of the principal species.

Many accounts have been given of real or supposed improvements in the tractability of polyesters conferred by copolymerisation.

Some polyesters, such as Table 3.3 (11a), have been mentioned earlier as being too high-melting to be admissible for fabrication by extrusion without suffering extensive thermal decomposition. By random copolymerisation the melting points can be brought down to levels where spinning, moulding, etc. become possible,[17,18] although to achieve this the required degree of modification may be so large as to yield products no longer of special interest. Even where, as with poly(ethylene terephthalate), processing presents no special problems, it has been suggested that film formation is facilitated by copolymerisation with groups such as isophthalate[19] or isopropylidene-di-*p*-phenoxyethyl[20]—an effect which is ascribed to the wider temperature ranges over which the copolymers soften, and to their slower crystallisation rates. Films of such polyesters have been claimed to display improvements in such physical properties as low-temperature flexibility and abrasion resistance, but the high-temperature properties must necessarily be impaired. It has also been asserted, though the evidence is by no means clear-cut, that the incorporation of small proportions (2–5 moles %) of adipate or cyclohexane-1,4-dicarboxylate residues into poly-(ethylene terephthalate) improves the fibre-forming characteristics by allowing easier drawing in a way which does not occur with equivalent amounts of copolymerised sebacate.[21,22] The difference is suggested to be due to the closer molecular resemblance of the supposedly effective groups to terephthalate than occurs with sebacate.

Corresponding with the lowering of crystallinity, copolymerisa-tion causes an increase in the solubilities of copolyesters in organic liquids as compared with the homopolymers. Copoly(ethylene isophthalate/terephthalate) having from 25% to 85% of combined isophthalate groups is thus soluble in various ketone, ester, ether, and chlorinated compounds which do not dissolve the related homopolyesters, and can therefore be cast as films or applied as coatings from solutions;[19] similar effects have been claimed for many other types of copolyesters.

The results of modifying the regularity of internal structure in polyesters are well displayed in connection with the dyeing pro-perties of copolyester fibres. Although the equilibrium uptake of dispersed dyes by polyester fibres is high, the rate of absorption (as discussed in Section 3.3.4) requires the provision of special measures to be brought to a technically satisfactory level. The rate of dye-uptake by poly(ethylene terephthalate) fibres is diminished by setting at high temperatures or by stretching to higher draw-ratios, both being processes which increase the extent and perfection of crystallinity. It is therefore obvious why the introduction of 'foreign' units into the molecular chains should cause an opposite effect, particularly when flexible aliphatic units or laterally bulky groups are incorporated to 'loosen' the structure, with a consequent enhancement of the rate of dyeing.[23-26] When the intruding entity also contains groups which are more strongly polar than the simple ester variety, the affinity for dispersed dyes may be increased still further.[27-30] At the present time there is considerable experiment with such modified polyester fibres within the textile industry where the balance of advantage between the improved dyeability and the concomitant expense, technical complications, and possible adverse effects upon the physical and thermomechanical properties remains to be fully assessed.

Investigations of copolyester modifications for improved dyeability in fibres have been extended to the incorporation of groups having specific affinities for classes of dyes other than the dispersed type. One variant, currently being offered as a speciality fibre in the United States under the trade name Dacron 64, is believed to be a copolymer of ethylene terephthalate contining sulphoisophthalate groups. The sulpho-groups (incorporated as metallic salts) have the power to combine by ion-exchange with the so-called 'basic dyes' which are mainly amine bases or ammonium or oxonium salts; similar effects are given by copolymeric units bearing other types of anionic groups as lateral appendages to the polymer chain or as end-groups.[31] Attempts have also been made to build amine-bearing groups into copolyesters to provide sites having affinity for the sulphonic acid dyes commonly used for cotton and wool,[32,33] but no technically satisfactory outcome has yet been reached to this end.

By introducing a large proportion of phosphorus-containing groups (e.g. $-OC \cdot \phi \cdot NH \cdot P(=O)Ph \cdot NH \cdot \phi \cdot CO-$) into polyesters, resins have been obtained which are claimed to possess retarded flammability.[34] The sulphonate-bearing copolyesters, in addition to their special dyeability, are also said to be more readily wetted, or coated, as films, with photographic emulsions.[35] Polyesters can be permanently coloured by copolymerisation with chromophoric components,[36] and chemical potentialities, such as that for cross-linking, may be introduced in appropriate functional groupings.[37] Whilst many of these examples are at the present no more than research curiosities, their range should serve to acquaint the reader with the possibilities, as well as with the limitations of random copolymers.

5.3 ORDERED COPOLYESTERS

The regularity of placement of molecular units in the chains of copolyesters would be expected to influence their characteristics in rather the same way as symmetry influences homopolyesters. The tendency for group-interchange between ester groups in polyester chains presents considerable difficulties for the preparation of ordered copolyesters of well-defined structures, thus few such compounds are known; but available information confirms the significance of structural regularity in connection with properties.

Of all types of ordered copolyesters the alternating binary ones are the least readily accessible. By the polymerisation of the macrocyclic lactone (Fig. 3.2 (b)), Goodman and Nesbitt obtained a crystalline, fibre-forming copolyester (T_m 177–180°C) whose properties were very different from those of the amorphous random copolyester of similar gross composition which could be made either by normal random copolymerisation or by heating the crystalline polymer in the molten state until structural randomisation had occurred by ester-ester interchange.[38] The crystalline polymer was considered to possess, or at least to contain substantial proportions of, the regularly alternating structure (Fig. 5.5 (a)), being thus of the (—AB—)$_n$ type. More specific syntheses of alternating terpolyesters, actually of the (—ABAC—)$_n$ type, were accomplished by the reaction of dicarboxylic acid chlorides with ethylene di-p-hydroxybenzoate, yielding the compounds (Fig. 5.5 (b)) having a variety of R groups.[39]

$$[-O \cdot (CH_2)_2 \cdot O \cdot OC \cdot \phi \cdot CO \cdot O \cdot (CH_2)_2 \cdot O \cdot (CH_2)_2 \cdot O \cdot OC \cdot \phi \cdot CO-]_n$$
(a)

$$[-OC \cdot R \cdot CO \cdot O \cdot \phi \cdot CO \cdot O \cdot (CH_2)_2 \cdot O \cdot OC \cdot \phi \cdot O-]_n$$
(b)

Fig. 5.5

The terephthalate and sebacate members of this series (R = ϕ or $(CH_2)_8$) were highly crystalline, melting above 360°C and at 115–120°C, respectively, whereas the random copolyesters of the same gross composition were an amorphous glass (R = ϕ) and a viscous syrup (R = $(CH_2)_8$), respectively. Somewhat similar findings applied to polycarbonates analogous to Fig. 5.5 (b).[40] These findings, taken together with corresponding ones for other classes of polymers, point to the rather special character of alternating copolymers which are perhaps best regarded as homopolymers of the whole complex repeating units present.

More conventional types of ordered copolyesters, namely the block copolyesters, have been prepared in two different ways. The simplest, but also the least specific, comprised heating different polyesters together in the molten state so that structural randomisation occurred, as could be followed by the changes in melting points.[41] In the limit, such processes must yield random copolyesters; but the earlier stages give block copolyesters having properties intermediate between those of the polyester mixtures and the fully randomised products. The rate of interchange is too great, however, to give materials of well-defined structures for study.

The second approach is based upon the use of pre-formed polymers, the individual blocks, furnished with end-groups suitable for linking into a polyester structure. Thus the reaction of hydroxyl-terminated poly(decamethylene isophthalate) with acid chloride-terminated poly(decamethylene terephthalate) gave a copolyester made of alternating blocks of the two species used.[42] The product was crystalline, in distinction to the equivalent random copolymer; its melting point (125–128°C) and that of the analogous tetramethylene block copolymer (213–215°C) suggest that the crystallinities were of the poly(alkylene terephthalate) type. A similar principle has been used to produce a variant of poly(ethylene terephthalate) made of blocks of this substance, each of molecular weight about 6,000, linked by isophthalate groups.[43]

Coleman[44] took advantage of the reactivity of the terminal hydroxyl groups in the Carbowax polyethers

$$HO \cdot [CH_2 \cdot CH_2 \cdot O]_n \cdot H$$

to obtain copolymers of ethylene terephthalate having substantial stretches of polyethyleneoxy units combined in the molecular chains, thus:

$$\sim\!O \cdot CH_2 \cdot CH_2 \cdot O \cdot OC \cdot \phi \cdot CO \cdot O \cdot [CH_2CH_2 \cdot O]_n \cdot OC \cdot \phi \cdot CO \cdot O \cdot CH_2 \cdot CH_2 \cdot O\!\sim$$

The properties of the products, whose crystallinity was solely of the poly(ethylene terephthalate) type, showed clearly the importance of the *molar* fraction, since, for given *weight* percentages of the polyether components, the melting points of the copolymers were determined by the sizes (i.e. molecular weights) of the polyether blocks; a block copolyester of this sort made with a content of 10% by weight of Carbowax residues of molecular weight 6,000 had a melting point little different from that of the normal homopolyester, whereas a similar amount of a simpler species, such as the 3-oxapentamethylene group, would, of course, have given a considerable depression. However, whilst the crystalline properties of these materials, their capacity for fibre formation, and the simple tensile properties of the fibres, were little altered, the characteristics of the amorphous regions in which the polyethyleneoxy segments were located were modified considerably so that the glass transition temperatures were reduced and fibres of the copolymers had a considerably enhanced dyeability and moisture absorbency. It has subsequently been found that similar effects are produced with copolymerised polyether blocks derived from monohydroxylic starting materials, $RO \cdot [CH_2 \cdot CH_2 \cdot O]_n H$, when the flexible segments are terminal to the polymeric terephthalate chains; in such cases it may also be necessary to incorporate small proportions of tri- or tetra-functional reagents which, through chain-branching, will serve to provide sufficiently large molecules for fibre formation.[45]

Despite their apparently interesting properties, the materials just discussed have not been accepted as sources of textile materials, mainly on account of the instability shown by their fibres on prolonged exposure to light. Nevertheless, they illustrate the types of differences to be expected between block and random copolyesters, and some later developments based on this concept are described in Section 5.5.

Graft copolymers based upon poly(ethylene terephthalate) have been mentioned in a number of publications. The procedure commonly used for their preparation involves the initial activation of the polyester substrate by such means as bombardment with accelerated electrons,[46,47] irradiation with γ-rays,[48–51] or mild thermal oxidation,[52] whereby reactive sites such as free radicals or peroxy groups are formed on the surface or in the bulk of the polyester which is then able to initiate the polymerisation of suitable monomers to form new chains chemically combined with atoms of the original material. Chains of units derived from acrylonitrile, potassium acrylate, vinyl esters, and styrene have been attached in this way. In a slightly varied procedure, polyester samples wetted with amines or polyethers are irradiated, when combination also occurs, probably between radicals generated in both the polyester and the agent of treatment. Since aromatic polyesters are relatively resistant to the effects of ionising radiations and to atmospheric oxidation, the degree of modification which can thus be attained is small, being mainly restricted to the surface of the material, for which reason this type of grafting has been proposed as a means of altering the superficial properties of films, fibres, or fabrics.   Although such treatments have been claimed to improve the surface dyeability, the capacity for adhesion to other materials and the ease of dispersion of static charge, there is no sign at present of their technical utilisation.

A different type of graft copolymer was described by Coleman

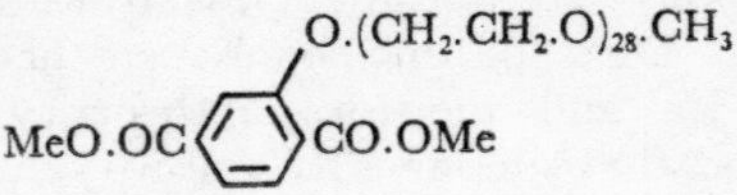

$$O.(CH_2.CH_2.O)_{28}.CH_3$$

$$MeO.OC \underset{}{\diagup}\!\!\!\!\diagdown CO.OMe$$

Fig. 5.6

as the product of incorporating a proportion of the compound shown in Fig. 5.6, with the normal ingredients for making poly(ethylene terephthalate).   Fibres of this product closely resembled those of the analogous block copolyesters, but the difficult accessibility of the copolymeric constituent excluded the material from practical interest.[44]   Graft copolymers have also been made in which polyester chains form the grafted 'branches' attached to polymers of different backbone structures,[53] but relatively little is yet known of their properties.

5.4   MODIFIED POLYESTERS

In all of the above cases the properties of polyesters have been altered as a result of changes in their chemical structures, but there are also instances where the properties—usually the dyeability of fibres—have been modified as a result of treatments with substances which, so far as is known, do not alter the chemical composition of the material and which must therefore be supposed to operate simply by dilation of the internal structure, perhaps by swelling the molecular voids, so that the amorphous regions are rendered more freely penetrable by dyestuff molecules.   These effects are to be distinguished from the plasticisation of normally stiff polymers insofar as the treating agents here do not remain within the material.

Improved dyeabilities have thus been claimed to result from the treatment of poly(ethylene terephthalate) fibres with hot dioxan,[54] and from the incorporation of diphenoxyethane into the polymer prior to conversion to fibres.[55]   A similar result follows the treatment of the fibres with chemicals such as phosphorus oxychloride or methanedisulphonyl chloride, the adhering portion of which is then hydrolysed by water and washed from the fibres.[56]   Other chemical substances which have been applied either to the polymer or to fibres to increase the affinity for dyes include N,N'-diphenyl-ethylenediamine in conjunction with chelatable metal compounds,[57] Schiff's bases,[58] and organosilicon compounds,[59] whilst the application of Carbowax polyethers to the undrawn fibres gives, after orientation, filaments which possess a modified skin with a glass-transition temperature lower than that of the unaffected core, and which are also more dyeable.[60] A comparative account of the technological effects of some of these processes, as well as of the effects of controlled degradation of fibres with various reagents, is given by Grunewald.[61]

5.5 ELASTOMERIC COPOLYESTERS AND COPOLYESTERURETHANES

In Section 5.3 was given a preliminary discussion of the properties of block copolymers comprised wholly or partly of polyester segments. This subject is now resumed with particular reference to polyester based copolymers having rubber-like characteristics where, in addition to the intrinsic practical interest, some further fascinating relationships between molecular structure and mechanical properties are displayed.

When typical high-melting aromatic polyesters are copolymerised randomly with large proportions (40–70%) of higher aliphatic dicarboxylic acid residues, the products may show elastomeric properties,[62, 63] although linear in structure and convertible to fibres. As an example, copoly(ethylene terephthalate/azelate) (49:51) was spun to fibres which were drawn fourfold and stabilised by heating at constant length at 110°C to give highly elastic yarns with a tenacity of 0·94 g/den., and extensibility to break of 302%, and a recovery from 100% extension of 96%.

Interesting as these properties were, the low melting points of such extensively copolymerised polyesters and their poor resistance towards attack by solvents and chemicals precluded any useful application.

The block copolyesters of Carbowax with ethylene terephthalate described above contained no more than 25% by weight of the polyethyleneoxy material, and apart from their modified dyeing and water absorbency properties they substantially resembled poly-(ethylene terephthalate) in being materials of normal modulus which yielded conventional fibres on spinning.[44] Charch and Shivers[64] extended this study by using higher proportions of the polyether component, and found that when this comprised 40–70% of the weight of the copolyesters, long-range elastic properties were again induced; however, owing to the dependence of melting point upon the molar fractional composition, these products had considerably higher melting points than the random copolymers mentioned in the preceding paragraphs. Thus, a copolymer of ethylene terephthalate containing 40% (by weight) of this component and 60% of polyethyleneoxy terephthalate blocks derived from polyether-diol of molecular weight 4,000 had a melting point near to 200°C, and gave fibres with extensibilities of over 300%, tensile recoveries of over 95%, and a low short-term stress-decay.

This work demonstrated that fibrous elastomeric materials can be obtained by the successive linear combination of blocks of stiff-chain crystallising polymers of high melting point with blocks of low-melting or poorly crystallising flexible-chain polymers having low glass-rubber transition temperatures. The molecular chains of the flexible segments were considered to be coiled randomly in the relaxed fibres, but to be capable of reversible extension under a cyclic strain. That the materials resist viscous flow can be ascribed to the spatial localisation provided in the matrix of mobile molecular chains by crystallites of the stiff-chain component, which here serve the same function as do the chemical cross-linkages in conventional rubbers.

This concept, the generation of elastomeric properties in linear copolymers composed of 'hard' and 'soft' segments as distinct from the conventional network structure in all-'soft' rubbery polymers, has been developed extensively in recent years in polymers of many different classes, and the voluminous patent literature (now amounting to several hundreds of specifications) indicates possibilities for employing linear polyesters of appropriate structure in either type of segment. Elastomers, both as fibres and bulk-rubbers, based upon the block copolymer principle are now articles of commerce, but, since the constitutions of the fibrous varieties have not been disclosed, it is impossible to state with certainty whether these include polyester members.

So far as the practical polyester-based elastomers are concerned, the details are more properly part of contemporary polyurethane technology, and in view of its complexity only a basic outline of the field can be given here, the interested reader being referred to other sources for a more comprehensive treatment.[65-70]

The origins of the subject are to be found in the polyester-based urethane rubbers (Vulkollan, sometimes spelt Vulcollan) which were developed as a result of investigations during and after World War II upon the reactions of isocyanates.[71,72] Typically, an aliphatic polyester of low molecular weight (approximately 2,000) having its chains terminated by hydroxyl groups was caused to react with an excess of naphthylene-1,5-diisocyanate whereby the polyester reacted as a diol to provide a macromolecular substance composed of polyester blocks connected through urethane groups

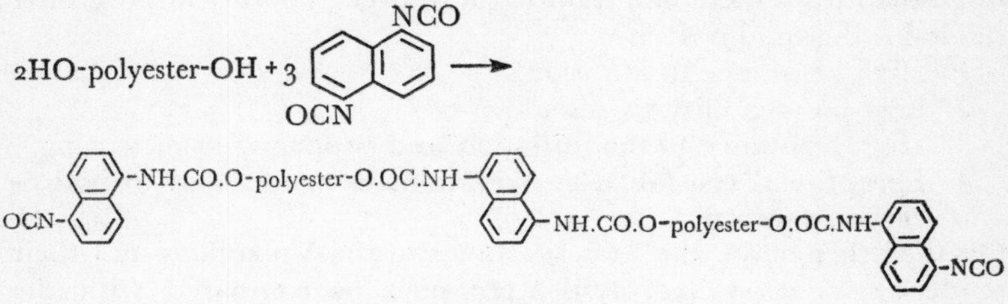

Fig. 5.7

(see Fig. 5.7). The proportions of reactants were so adjusted that two or three polyester blocks became combined in each complex chain which was terminated by an unreacted isocyanate group (—NCO). In a subsequent stage the product was treated under controlled conditions with limited amounts of water (other reagents such as diols, diamines, dicarboxylic acids, or amino-alcohols could also be used) when chain-extension occurred by the conversion of *some* of the free isocyanate groups to urea linkages:

$$\sim\!\!\sim\!\text{NCO} + \text{H}_2\text{O} + \text{OCN}\!\sim\!\!\sim \longrightarrow \sim\!\!\sim\!\text{NH}\cdot\text{CO}\cdot\text{NH}\!\sim\!\!\sim + \text{CO}_2$$

The remaining isocyanate groups then reacted at a higher temperature with the already-formed urea groups to form biurets which, on account of the distribution of reacting centres throughout the mass, constituted the chemical cross-linkages shown in Fig. 5.8.

Fig. 5.8

(The wavy lines here represent the polyester-block copolymers terminated by naphthylene groups.) The polyesters most favoured for use in this application were poly(ethylene adipate) and copoly-(ethylene/1,2-propylene adipate) whose melting and glass-transition temperatures were sufficiently low to give a mobile molecular character to the whole material.

Procedures were developed for the manipulation of the Vulkollans by conventional rubber technological processes as well as by solvent or liquid-casting methods. The tensile properties of the products resembled those of natural rubbers but they were distinguished from these in a number of respects, notably in possessing the following qualities:

1. High resistance to abrasion.
2. Low permeability to gases.
3. High resistance to the initiation and propagation of tearing.
4. Exceptional resistance to oxidation, to ozone, and to hydrocarbon solvents.

On the other hand, the heat resistance of the Vulkollans and their tendency to resist hydrolysis were poor as compared with the traditional rubbers and vinyl elastomers. In the highly competitive situation of recent years these relatively expensive materials have made little advance as compared with other novel elastomers but, as mentioned in Section 1.3, they find application in some speciality outlets. The American products Chemigum SL and Paraplex X100 are also understood to be rubbers of the polyester class, the former being a copolyurethane and the latter a peroxide crosslinked material.

Unlike these products, the elastomeric copolyesterurethane fibres are believed to possess mainly linear chain structures. Many variations of materials and procedure have been described,[73-77] but it is again common to react hydroxyl-terminated low molecular weight polyesters with excess of a diisocyanate, often diphenylmethane-4,4'-diisocyanate rather than the naphthylene compound used for the bulk-rubbers, to give an isocyanate-terminated composition made of two or three urethane-linked polyester blocks, which is dissolved in an inert solvent such as dimethylformamide and then treated in one or other of two ways. The solution is either (i) treated with a reactive diamine (hydrazine, ethylenediamine, piperazines, etc.), which causes chain-extension by combination with the isocyanate end-groups and with any residual free diisocyanate yielding a high polymer, still in solution, from which fibres are made by dry-spinning (i.e. extrusion into a current of heated air which evaporates the solvent and leaves the material in filamentary form), or (ii) extruded through spinneret holes into an aqueous diamine solution, when the urea-forming reaction occurs with coagulation at the surfaces of the fine cylindrical streams of the spun material, and self-supporting filaments are obtained which are finally cured by heating with water. Part of the molecular chain-structure of such products may be represented as follows:

$\sim$NH·CO·O—polyester—O·OC·NH·R·NH·CO·O—polyester—

—O·OC·NH·R·NH·CO·NH·R′·NH·CO·NH·R·NH·CO·O—polyester$\sim$

Here R may be —ϕ·CH$_2$·ϕ— and R′ is derived from the chain-extending diamine, being a direct linkage when hydrazine is used and (CH$_2$)$_2$ when ethylenediamine is the reagent of choice; the polyester blocks are again commonly selected from the low-melting aliphatic polyester or copolyester group. The technology associated with these processes is naturally very complex, and the details will vary depending upon the particular composition and system used.

A typical copolyesterurethane fibre made according to these principles from poly(ethylene adipate) as the block component had a tenacity of 0·63 g/den., an extensibility of 630%, and an initial modulus of 0·06 g/den., properties which are fairly representative for the whole class of products. On account of the presence of the urethane and urea groups, these fibres have considerably higher melting points than are readily attainable when polyester blocks are used as the 'hard' segments,[78] and they have many virtues, e.g. dyeability, good abrasion resistance, and inertness to cosmetic oils and to perspiration, which allows them to be used advantageously in place of the traditional cotton-coated rubber filaments in swimwear, foundation garments, and similar clothing. Fibres of this sort are included in the 'spandex' group, defined by the U.S. Federal Trade Commission as manufactured fibres in which the fibre-forming substance is any long-chain synthetic polymer composed of at least 85% by weight of a segmented polyurethane.

The principles of copolyesterurethane formation can also be adapted to the manufacture of flexible or rigid foams, but the starting materials for these are branched or partially cross-linked polyesters which are outside the scope of Volume I.

5.6 POLYESTERAMIDES

Early in the history of the linear aliphatic polyesters efforts were made to ameliorate their low melting points by copolymerising amide-forming substances with the polyester-building materials. Thus, copolymers from propane-1,3-diol, hexadecamethylene-dicarboxylic acid, and 6-aminocaproic acid had melting points which increased from that of the polyester in proportion to the amount of amino-acid used.[79]

Such products, which on account of their constituent groups are known as polyesteramides, have properties between those of the related polyesters and polyamides, and when prepared in this way are most probably random copolymers. Subsequently it has been recognised that diols or dicarboxylic compounds containing preformed amide groups can be employed as normal starting materials for polyesterification reactions, giving crystalline polyesteramides of regular structures, and a representative selection of such polymers is given in Table 5.1.

Although a wide range of structures is exemplified, the melting points lie within a relatively narrow range, but they are higher than those of random polyesteramides of similar overall composition, and considerably higher than those foreseen for the analogous polyesters having —O— in place of —NH—.

Izard,[88] who studied copolyesteramides of poly(hexamethylene decane-1,10-dicarboxylate) with various combined proportions of —NH·(CH$_2$)$_6$·NH— or of —NH·CH$_2$·ϕ·CH$_2$·NH— groups, ascribed the monotonic change of melting points with composition in the first case, and the eutectic-type change in the second, to differences between the sizes of the diamine residues. There are too few data to confirm whether near-isomorphism of groups is a reliable determinant of the shapes of melting point *versus* composition diagrams in polyesteramides, and in at least one other series— the copolyesteramides of hexane 1,6-diol with terephthalic acid and 1,6-di-*p*-carboxybenzamidohexane where the combined groups have very different molecular sizes—the changes of melting point with composition do not produce a minimum value between those of the terminal polymers.[89]

Whilst polyesteramides of the types described, and their copolymers with polyesters, are generally convertible to strong fibres and films, these are not known to display any specially meritorious features which cannot be reproduced in the polyesters and polyamides separately, and in view of their chemically complex structures no commercial development has been undertaken. However, an elastomeric material of the copolyesteramide/urethane type, Vulcaprene A, has been used for some years in this country as a basis for coatings, adhesives, and rubber varnishes.[90-92] Vulcaprene A is manufactured by the co-condensation of ethanolamine, ethylene glycol, and adipic acid to a low polymer (molecular weight 5,000–10,000) which is caused to react with a diisocyanate

Table 5.1 POLYESTERAMIDES OF REGULARLY ALTERNATING STRUCTURE

Repeat-Unit	T_m(°C)	Ref.
—OC·(CH₂)₂·S·(CH₂)₂·CO·O·(CH₂)₂·CO·NH·(CH₂)₆·CO·NH·CO·(CH₂)₆·O—	140	80
—O·(CH₂)₂·O·OC·(CH₂)₆·NH·CO·CO·NH·(CH₂)₆·CO—	165	81
—O·(CH₂)₄·O·OC·(CH₂)₄·CO·NH·CH₂·φ·CH₂·NH·CO·(CH₂)₄·CO—	208	82
—O·(CH₂)₅·O·OC·φ·CO·NH·φ·CO—	215	83
—O·(CH₂)₂·O·OC·(CH₂)₅·NH·CO·φ·CO·NH·(CH₂)₅·CO—	213–216	84
—OC·φ·CO·O·(CH₂)₆·CO·NH·(CH₂)₆·NH·CO·(CH₂)₆·O—	230	80
—O·(CH₂)₆·O·OC·φ·CO·N⟨ring⟩N·CO·φ·CO—	255	85
—O·(CH₂)₄·O·OC·φ·NH·CO·(CH₂)₆·CO·NH·φ·CO—	265	86
—O·(CH₂)₆·O·OC·φ·CO·NH·CH₂·φ·CH₂·NH·CO·φ·CO—	285	82
—O·(CH₂)₄·O·OC·φ·CO·NH·(CH₂)₆·NH·CO·φ·CO—	300	87

for chain-lengthening and then finally cured by further reaction with a diisocyanate or with a formaldehyde-generating substance. Whilst the material could be used as the basis of a bulk elastomer, its main interest arose from the ease with which it could be compounded with other polymers—including nitrocellulose, poly(vinyl formal), cellulose acetate, degraded vegetable-tanned leather, etc.—and with solvents, to give solutions or doughs which were applied in leathercloth coatings, proofings, paper protection paints, and a variety of other uses.   As with polyester rubbers generally, Vulcaprene products possessed an outstanding resistance to attack by oxygen, ozone, petrol, and hydrocarbon oils, but they are not suitable for use in hot moist conditions and are now being superseded by polyether-based urethane compositions.

5.7   POLYESTERS OF PHOSPHORUS AND SULPHUR OXYACIDS

Some polybasic oxyacid derivatives of phosphorus and sulphur resemble the oxyacids of carbon (carbonic acid or dicarboxylic acids) in that they can be converted to linear chain polyesters.

The phosphorus compounds of these types which have been prepared are the polyphosphonates (Fig. 5.9 (a), R = H or a hydrocarbon group, R' = alkylene or arylene),[93-97] the polyphosphates (Fig. 5.9 (b)),[98] and the polyphosphites (Fig. 5.9 (c)).[99]

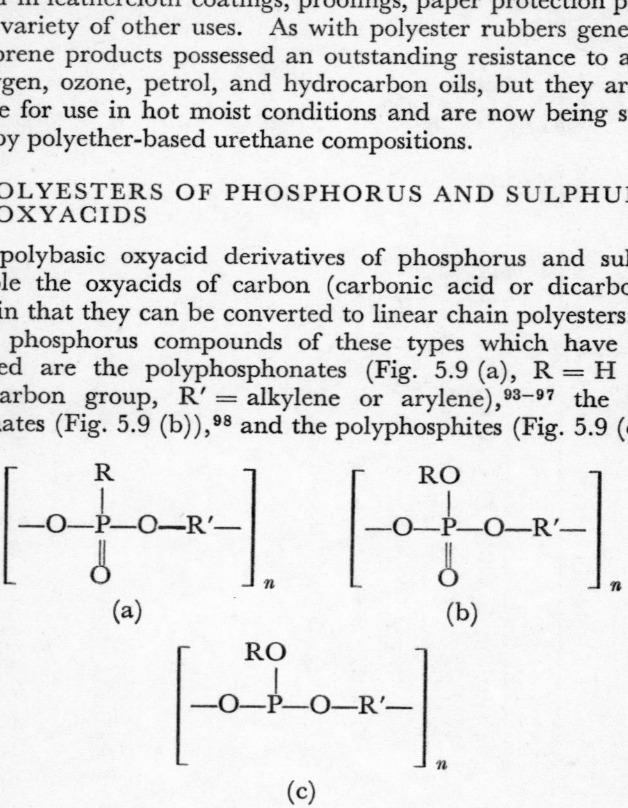

$$\left[-O-\underset{\underset{O}{\|}}{\overset{\overset{R}{|}}{P}}-O-R'- \right]_n \qquad \left[-O-\underset{\underset{O}{\|}}{\overset{\overset{RO}{|}}{P}}-O-R'- \right]_n$$

(a)   (b)

$$\left[-O-\underset{}{\overset{\overset{RO}{|}}{P}}-O-R'- \right]_n$$

(c)

Fig. 5.9

The techniques of preparation include the reactions of diols with phosphonic dichlorides or phosphonic esters, and the polymerisation of cyclic phosphites or phosphonates, these being analogous to methods used for carboxylic polyesters, and there is one additional

Table 5.2 SOFTENING POINTS OF SOME POLYSULPHONATES

Repeat Unit	Softening Point (°C)
$-O_2S \cdot \phi \cdot \phi \cdot SO_2 \cdot O \cdot \phi \cdot CMe_2 \cdot \phi \cdot O-$	160–165
	110–115
	100–105
	140–170
	197–200
$-O_2S \cdot \phi \cdot CH_2 \cdot \phi \cdot SO_2 \cdot O \cdot \phi \cdot CMe_2 \cdot \phi \cdot O-$	114–116
$-O_2S \cdot \phi \cdot O \cdot \phi \cdot SO_2 \cdot O \cdot \phi \cdot CMe_2 \cdot \phi \cdot O-$	118–120
$-O_2S \cdot \phi \cdot CO \cdot O \cdot \phi \cdot CMe_2 \cdot \phi \cdot O-$	155
	122

reaction—the polymerisation of bis-2-chloroethyl phosphonates through the elimination of ethylene dichloride—which has no counterpart in the carbon series.[98] The properties of these polyesters can be summarised simply insofar as all those known are amorphous substances, being either viscous syrups or glassy resins with softening points no higher than 130°C. They are generally readily soluble in organic solvents, though not in water, and are often described as non-flammable substances. The chain extension of some of these polyesters with diisocyanates to give solid products has also been described.[97]

The known sulphonic analogues of carboxylic polyesters are all polymeric disulphonates (Fig. 5.10), made by the reaction of dichlorides of disulphonic acids

$$[-O_2S \cdot R \cdot SO_2 \cdot O \cdot R' \cdot O-]_n$$

Fig. 5.10

with dihydric phenols using the interfacial polycondensation method.[100,101] The polysulphonates are mostly readily soluble in chlorinated hydrocarbon solvents from which some members have been recovered in crystalline form. Normally, however, they are obtained as amorphous resins, and they can be converted to films having tensile strengths in the range of 6–9 kg/mm², yield strengths of 5–7 kg/mm², extensibilities of 2–6%, and moduli of elasticity of 240–320 kg/mm². Their softening points vary with structure, being mainly in the range 80–200°C. A sufficient number of polysulphonates has been described to show that the structural factors which control the glass-transition temperatures and melting points of carboxylic polyesters also operate here, but the direct comparison of such polyesters as Table 3.4 (2) and Table 3.4 (3) with their sulphonate analogues shows the latter to have the lower softening temperatures. Representative polysulphonates and polycarboxylate/sulphonates are given in Table 5.2.

5.8   SUGGESTIONS FOR FURTHER READING

The treatment of the subject given in the foregoing text is necessarily selective, being prone to reflect the preoccupations and perhaps the inadvertent prejudices of the author. References have therefore been selected, wherever possible, as guides to further sources, and the reader is counselled to make full use of them to amplify the factual and theoretical background. Four works under references 102–105 will be found particularly useful in this respect, and a bibliography[106] published in 1956, though obviously unsuitable for recent work, will be helpful in leading to earlier references.

Much valuable information on the practical aspects of the chemical synthesis of polyesters can be gained from the laboratory manual of Sorenson and Campbell,[107] and from a volume of Houben-Weyl's standard organic chemical treatise,[108] whilst a comparative account of the molecular structure and the formation of fibres is available in books dealing with this subject.[109,110]

The technical literature of the manufacturers of polyester films and fibres is freely available and is generally written objectively and with a wealth of practical data; it should be consulted on all questions of technical fabrication and use. The annual volumes of the Reports on the Progress of Applied Chemistry and the Review of Textile Progress, published by the Society of the Chemical Industry and the Textile Institute, respectively, also normally contain articles dealing with developments in the raw materials for polyesters and with the polymers themselves.

Lastly, the reader with a command of the Russian language will find interest in a booklet by Petukhov[111] dealing with the technical manufacture of poly(ethylene terephthalate) and its conversion to fibres,* and in the monograph by Korshak and Vinogradova[112] which gives an extensive coverage of the topic of polyesters, though —in the present author's view—on a somewhat uncritical basis.

*Since the above was written, an English translation of Petukhov's book has become available under the title 'The Technology of Polyester Fibres' (Pergamon Press, Oxford, 1963).

REFERENCES

(1) BUNGS, J. A. (Diamond Alkali Company), U.S. Pat. 2,967,854
(2) DOAK, K. W., and CAMPBELL, H. N., *J. Polymer Sci.*, **18**, 215 (1955)
(3) WIELICKI, E. A., BOONE, C. J., EVANS, R. D., LYTTON, M. R., SUMMERS, H. B., and HEDRICK, G. W., *J. Polymer Sci.*, **38**, 307 (1959)
(4) MARTIN, E. V., *Textile Res. J.*, **32**, 619 (1962)
(5) FULLER, C. S., *J. Amer. Chem. Soc.*, **70**, 421 (1948)
(6) EDGAR, O. B., and ELLERY, E., *J. Chem. Soc.*, 2633 (1952)
(7) GOODMAN, I., and MILBURN, A. H. (unpublished work)
(8) GOLIKE, R. C., and COBBS, W. H., *J. Polymer Sci.*, **54**, 277 (1961)
(9) KORSHAK, V. V., GOLUBEV, V. V., KARPOVA, G. V., and DUBOVA, T. A., *Izvest. Akad. Nauk S.S.S.R., Otdel. Khim. Nauk*, 540 (1959)
(10) FLORY, P. J., *Principles of Polymer Chemistry*, Cornell University Press, Ithaca, New York, Chap. XIII (1953)
(11) CRAMER, F. B. (E. I. du Pont de Nemours and Company), U.S. Pat. 3,070,575
(12) SMITH, C. W., and DOLE, M., *J. Polymer Sci.*, **20**, 37 (1956)
(13) KOREMATSU, M., MASUDA, H., and KURIYAMA, S., *Kogyo Kagaku Zasshi*, **63**, 884 (1960)
(14) WUNDERLICH, B., and DOLE, M., *J. Polymer Sci.*, **32**, 125 (1958)

(15) CONIX, A., and VAN KERPEL, R., *J. Polymer Sci.*, **40**, 521 (1959)
(16) EDGAR, O. B., *J. Chem. Soc.*, 2638 (1952)
(17) WIELICKI, E. A., and EVANS, R. D. (American Viscose Corporation), U.S. Pats. 3,008,930–1; 3,008,933–5.
(18) LYTTON, M. L., and WIELICKI, E. A. (American Viscose Corporation), French Pat. 1,181,102
(19) The Goodyear Tire and Rubber Company, Brit. Pat. 766,290
(20) The Goodyear Tire and Rubber Company, Brit. Pat. 877,539
(21) PETUKHOV, B. V., and KONDRASHOVA, S. M., *Vysokomolekul. Soedin*, **3**, 657 (1961)
(22) PETUKHOV, B. V., and KONDRASHOVA, S. M., *Khim. Volokna*, 10 (1962)
(23) STIMPSON, J. W., MUNRO, N., and GOODMAN. I. (Imperial Chemical Industries Limited), Brit. Pat. 885,739
(24) Badische Anilin- & Soda Fabrik A.G. Brit. Pat. 793,907
(25) Inventa A.G. für Forschung und Patentverwertung, Brit. Pat. 908,970
(26) GELEJI, F., HOLLY, Z., and DONBROVSZKY, S., *Faserforsch. Textiltech.*, **13**, 490 (1962)
(27) HORN, C. F. (Union Carbide Corporation), Brit. Pat. 873,862
(28) CALDWELL, J. R. and DANNELLY, C. R. (Eastman Kodak Company), U.S. Pat. 2,945,009
(29) CALDWELL, J. R., and WELLMAN, J. W. (Eastman Kodak Company), U.S. Pats. 2,899,408; 2,925,404
(30) CALDWELL, J. R. (Eastman Kodak Company), U.S. Pat. 2,852,491
(31) E. I. du Pont de Nemours and Company, Brit. Pats. 856,917; 868,496
(32) SHIVERS, J. C. (E. I. du Pont de Nemours and Company), U.S. Pats. 2,647,104; 2,777,830
(33) LINCOLN, J., HAMMOND, K. M., and GROOMBRIDGE, W. H. (British Celanese Ltd.), U.S. Pat. 2,739,958
(34) CALDWELL, J. R., and MARTIN, J. C. (Eastman Kodak Company), U.S. Pat. 2,882,294
(35) E. I. du Pont de Nemours and Company, Brit. Pat. 884,290
(36) MCINTYRE, J. E., and PUGH, E. C. (Imperial Chemical Industries Ltd.), Brit. Pat. 838,716
(37) ANDERSON, J. L. (E. I. du Pont de Nemours and Company), Deutsche Auslegeschrift 1,100,967
(38) GOODMAN, I., and NESBITT, B. F., *J. Polymer Sci.*, **47**, 423 (1960)
(39) GOODMAN, I., and HADDOCK, E. (Imperial Chemical Industries Limited), Brit. Pat. 968,390
(40) Inventa A.G. für Forschung und Patentverwertung, Brit. Pat. 908,851
(41) KRESSE, P., *Faserforsch. Textiltech.*, **11**, 353 (1960)
(42) FLORY, P. J. (The Goodyear Tire and Rubber Co.), U.S. Pat. 2,691,006
(43) Wingfoot Corporation, British Pat. 728,550
(44) COLEMAN, D., *J. Polymer Sci.*, **14**, 15 (1954)
(45) The Chemstrand Corporation, Brit. Pat. 847,090
(46) CLINE, E. T., and TANNER, D. (E. I. du Pont de Nemours and Company), Belgian Pat. 555,531
(47) CLINE, E. T., and TANNER, D. (E. I. du Pont de Nemours and Company), Canadian Pat. 621,543
(48) BEVINGTON, J. C., and EVANS, D. E., *Nature, Lond.*, **178**, 1112 (1956)
(49) TANNER, D., and MAGAT, E. E. (E. I. du Pont de Nemours and Company), Belgian Pat. 546,815
(50) Société des Usines Chimiques Rhone-Poulenc, Brit. Pat. 850,446
(51) E. I. du Pont de Nemours and Company, Brit. Pat. 838,412
(52) KORSHAK, V. V., MOZGOVA, K. K., and KRUKOVSKIĬ, S. P., *Vysokomolekul. Soedin.*, **4**, 1625 (1962)
(53) KOLESNIKOV, G. S., and HAN-MING, T., *Russian Chem. Rev.* (English trans.), **31**, 485 (1962)

Copolyesters, Modified Polyesters, and Related Compounds 139

(54) HAM, G. E., and BEINDORFF, A. B. (The Chemstrand Corporation), Belgian Pat. 546,423
(55) E. I. du Pont de Nemours and Company, Brit. Pat. 898,289
(56) Imperial Chemical Industries Limited, Belgian Pat. 586,792
(57) CALDWELL, J. R., and GILKEY, R. (Eastman Kodak Company), U.S. Pat. 2,945,010
(58) SELLE, H. D., and RUHNAU, A. (VEB Chemische Fabrik Grünau), U.S. Pat. 3,022,131
(59) Dow Corning Corporation, Brit. Pat. 923,394
(60) RICHARDS, G., TAYLOR, G. W., and PARKEY, W. D. (Imperial Chemical Industries Limited), Brit. Pat. 919,860
(61) GRUNEWALD, H., *Melliand Textilber.*, **43**, 48 (1962)
(62) E. I. du Pont de Nemours and Company, Brit. Pats. 711,279–280
(63) SNYDER, M. D. (E. I. du Pont de Nemours and Company), U.S. Pat. 2,623,033
(64) CHARCH, W. H., and SHIVERS, J. C., *Text. Res. J.*, **29**, 536 (1959)
(65) *Polyurethanes: Chemistry, Technology and Properties*, PHILLIPS, L. N., and PARKER. D. B. V., Iliffe, London (1964) (for the Plastics Institute)
(66) DOMBROW, B. A., *Polyurethanes*, Reinhold Publishing Corporation, New York (1957)
(67) WHITBY, G. S., DAVIS, C. C., and DUNBROOK, R. F. (Eds.), *Synthetic Rubbers*, John Wiley & Sons, Inc., New York, Chap. 25 (1954)
(68) KIRK, R. E., and OTHMER, D. F. (eds.), *Encyclopedia of Chemical Technology*, Supplement **Vol. 1**, 888, Interscience Encyclopedia Inc., New York (1957)
(69) RINKE, H., *Angew. Chem.*, **74**, 612 (1962)
(70) SAUNDERS, J. H., and FRISCH, K. C., *Polyurethanes; Chemistry and Technology*, Interscience Publishers, New York, Part 1 (1962), Part 2 (1964)
(71) BAYER, O., MÜLLER, E., PETERSEN, S., PIEPENBRINK, H. F., and WINDEMUTH, E., *Rubb. Chem. Technol.*, **23**, 812 (1950)
(72) MÜLLER, E., BAYER, O., PETERSEN, S., PIEPENBRINK, H. F., SCHMIDT, F., and WEINBRENNER, E., *Rubb. Chem. Technol.*, **26**, 493 (1953)
(73) FRANKENBURG, P. H., and FRAZER, A. H. (E. I. du Pont de Nemours and Co.), U.S. Pat. 2,957,852
(74) United States Rubber Company, Brit. Pats. 847,673; 854,476; 873,648; 879,638
(75) E. I. du Pont de Nemours and Company, Brit. Pats. 849,154; 881,635; U.S. Pat. 3,044,987
(76) Farbenfabriken Bayer A.G., Brit. Pat. 904,459
(77) YOUNG, D. M., and HOSTETTLER, F. (Union Carbide Corporation), U.S. Pat. 3,051,687
(78) SHIVERS, J. C. (E. I. du Pont de Nemours and Company), U.S. Pat. 3,023,192
(79) CAROTHERS, W. H., and HILL, J. W., *J. Amer. Chem. Soc.*, **54**, 1566 (1932)
(80) ROSE, J. K., and SCHULZ, H. W. (Union Carbide and Carbon Corporation), Brit. Pat. 777,398
(81) COLEMAN, D., and MCKAY, A. F. (Monsanto Canada Ltd.), U.S. Pat. 2,954,364
(82) REYNOLDS, D. D., and WILLIAMS, J. L. R. (Eastman Kodak Company), U.S. Pat. 2,956,984
(83) REYNOLDS, D. D., and LAAKSO, T. M. (Eastman Kodak Company), U.S. Pat. 2,794,795
(84) Farbenfabriken Bayer A.G., Brit. Pat. 747,031
(85) WILLIAMS, J. L. R., and LAAKSO, T. M. (Eastman Kodak Company), U.S. Pat. 2,852,492
(86) REYNOLDS, D. D., and LAAKSO, T. M. (Eastman Kodak Company), U.S. Pat. 2,848,439
(87) WILLIAMS, J. L. R., and LAAKSO, T. M. (Kodak-Pathé), French Pat. 1,152,249
(88) IZARD, E. F., *J. Polymer Sci.*, **8**, 503 (1952)
(89) WILLIAMS, J. L. R., and LAAKSO, T. M. (Eastman Kodak Company), U.S. Pat. 2,851,443
(90) HARPER, D. A., *Trans. Inst. Rubber Ind.*, **24**, 181 (1948)

(91) WHITE, H. G., *J. Oil Col. Chem. Ass.*, **32**, 461 (1949)
(92) HARPER, D. A., SMITH, W. F., and WHITE, H. G., *Proc. 2nd Rubb. Tech. Conf.*, 61 (1948)
(93) COOVER, H. W. (Eastman Kodak Company), U.S. Pat. 2,743,258
(94) ALBRIGHT AND WILSON (MFG.) LIMITED (Coates, H.), Brit. Pat. 796,446
(95) MCCORMACK, W. B., and SCHROEDER, H. E. (E. I. du Pont de Nemours and Co.), U.S. Pat. 2,891,915
(96) HAVEN, A. C., JR. (E. I. du Pont de Nemours and Company), U.S. Pat. 2,900,365
(97) MCCONNELL, R. L., and COOVER, H. W. (Eastman Kodak Company), U.S. Pat. 2,926,145
(98) KORSHAK, V. V., *J. Polymer Sci.*, **31**, 319 (1958)
(99) MCMANIMIE, R. J. (Monsanto Chemical Company), U.S. Pat. 2,893,961
(100) CONIX, A. J., and LARIDON, U. L. (Gevaert Photo-Producten N.V.), Brit. Pats. 916,660; 974,342; 975,813
(101) CONIX, A., and LARIDON, U., Paper presented at International Symposium on Macromolecules, I.U.P.A.C., Wiesbaden, 1959
(102) *Collected Papers of Wallace Hume Carothers*, MARK, H., and WHITBY, G. S. (eds.), Interscience Publishers Inc., New York (1940)
(103) KORSHAK, V. V., and VINOGRADOVA, S. V. *Russian Chem. Revs.* (English Trans.), **30**, 171 (1961)
(104) WILFONG, R. E., *J. Polymer Sci.*, **54**, 385 (1961)
(105) REYNOLDS, R. J. W., *Fibres from Synthetic Polymers*, HILL, R. (ed.), Elsevier Publishing Co., Amsterdam, Chap. 6 (1953)
(106) BJORKSTEN RESEARCH LABORATORIES INC., *Polyesters and Their Applications*, Reinhold Publishing Corporation, New York (1956)
(107) SORENSEN, W. R., and CAMPBELL, T. W., *Preparative Methods of Polymer Chemistry*, Interscience Publishers Inc., New York (1961)
(108) *Methoden der Organischen Chemie* (Houben-Weyl), MÜLLER, E. (ed.), 4th Edition: Band XIV/2, Makromolekulare Stoffe, Teil 2, G. Thieme Verlag, Stuttgart (1963)
(109) HEARLE, J. W. S., and PETERS, R. H. (eds.), *Fibre Structure*, The Textile Institute and Butterworths Ltd., London (1963)
(110) *High Polymers: Structure and Physical Properties*, 2nd Edition, GORDON, M., Iliffe, London (1963) (for the Plastics Institute)
(111) PETUKHOV, B. V., *Poliefirnoe Volokno (Terilen, Lavsan) (Polyester Fibres (Terylene, Lavsan))*, Goskhimizdat, Moscow (1960)
(112) KORSHAK, V. V., and VINOGRADOVA, S. V., *Geterotsepniye Poliefiri (Heterochain Polyesters)*, Izdatel'stvo Akademii Nauk S.S.S.R., Moscow (1958)

CHAPTER 6

POLYCARBONATES

6.1 INDUSTRIAL HISTORY

6.1.1 HISTORICAL DEVELOPMENT

This section deals with those polycarbonates in which the carbonate group —O·CO·O— is used for the building of the macromolecular chain. These are the true polyesters of carbonic acid: another group of polymers, derived by the polymerisation of unsaturated monomers such as vinyl or allyl carbonates, and in which the carbonate group does not take part in the polymer-building reaction, can also be termed polyesters, but have been excluded from the present discussion.

Polycarbonates have been known since the beginning of this century, though their true nature was not recognised: but they have only recently achieved commercial significance. In 1898 Einhorn[1] reported the formation of polycarbonates in the reaction of phosgene with three dihydric phenols. In 1902 Bischoff and Hedenström[2] confirmed this work using an ester-exchange reaction. These polycarbonates were intractable insoluble materials, and for many years the plastics industry showed no interest in their development, though admittedly Carothers[3] included aliphatic polycarbonates in his classical work on polyesters, and reported on these in 1930. There followed a considerable volume of work on aliphatic polyesters, none of which found any technical applications. It was not until 1956, when Schnell[4] described the work carried out at Farbenfabriken Bayer on aromatic polycarbonates, that any reference appeared in the literature to the materials which we now know as polycarbonates. At about the same time the Eastman Kodak

Company and the General Electric Company were working on the same lines.   Search was directed towards members of the family which would be tractable, resistant to hydrolysis, and thermally stable.   Polycarbonates based on the annexed compound have been

$$HO\!\!-\!\!\langle\ \rangle\!\!-\!\!R\!\!-\!\!\langle\ \rangle\!\!-\!\!OH$$

investigated very fully.   Here, R may contain alkyl or cycloalkyl groupings, and oxygen- or sulphur-containing groups: and the aromatic rings have been substituted in almost every kind of way. This work has been reported quite widely.   Remond,[5] Schnell,[4,6] Cottin,[7] and Thompson and Goldblum[8] have all covered a wide range of substituents in their papers.   Numerous patents have been published, covering halogen-containing compounds,[9] sulphoxide groups,[10] and ether linkages.[11]

Nevertheless the only products to be produced commercially were those based on 2,2-di(*p*-hydroxyphenyl) propane, usually termed Bisphenol A (i.e. the foregoing compound, where $R = CMe_2$). Many of the above products were superior to the Bisphenol A polycarbonate in some property, but no other polycarbonate had such a good balance of properties.   With the development of the epoxide resins, Bisphenol A was readily available commercially; added to this, techniques for handling difficult polymers had now been highly developed; consequently, the time was opportune for the development of Bisphenol A polycarbonates.   Materials became available for evaluation by 1958; full-scale production commenced in Germany in 1959, and in the U.S.A. in 1960.   Figures for world consumption are not available, but *Modern Plastics*[14] gave the following figures for the U.S.A.: 1960, 500,000 lb; 1961, 1,700,000 lb; 1962 (estimated), 7,000,000 lb.

For the present, this is the only polycarbonate of commercial significance, and it will be considered in detail hereafter.

6.2   MANUFACTURE

6.2.1   RAW MATERIALS

Polycarbonates are polyesters made from carbonic acid instead of the more usual organic acids such as phthalic, adipic, maleic, etc.

Carbonic acid itself does not, of course, take part in the normal esterification process; instead, its derivatives, such as phosgene or carbonic esters, have to be reacted with Bisphenol A. Other analogous compounds such as chlorocarbonic esters[12] and carbonyl diimidazole[13] have also been covered by patents.

6.2.1.1 *Phosgene*

Phosgene (also known as carbonyl chloride) is the acid chloride of carbonic acid, and is made by the direct union of carbon monoxide and chlorine. It is a gas which fumes in moist air, has a pungent, unpleasant, and suffocating smell, and condenses to a liquid at 8°C.

$$CO + Cl_2 \xrightarrow[\text{catalyst}]{\text{light or}} COCl_2$$

6.2.1.2 *Diphenyl Carbonate*

Diphenyl carbonate is a white crystalline solid, m.p. 78°C. It is therefore a more pleasant material to handle than phosgene, and in this application can be considered as a 'phosgene carrier'. It is made by reacting phosgene with two equivalents of the sodium salt of phenol.

$$COCl_2 + 2NaOPh \longrightarrow CO(OPh)_2 + 2NaCl$$

6.2.1.3 *Diethyl Carbonate*

This and other similar carbonates can be prepared either by the direct addition of phosgene to alcohol, or (for higher carbonates) by ester-interchange reactions in the presence of hydrochloric or sulphuric acid.

6.2.1.4 *Bisphenol A*

This substance, 2,2-di(*p*-hydroxyphenyl)propane, was first characterised in 1892 by Dianin,[15] who condensed phenol with acetone. The chemistry of this reaction has been dealt with very fully in the literature; the significant feature is that it can result in a number of isomers, together with trisphenol and certain chromogenic compounds. These may be present only in small amounts, which are not serious when Bisphenol A is used for epoxide resins, though even here the colour conferred on these resins may not be desirable; but when it is used for polycarbonate production, the results are much more serious. The trifunctional trisphenol introduces chain branching; the *ortho-para*, and *ortho-ortho* isomers upset chain symmetry; and the presence of colour-producing bodies make it impossible to produce the desired water-white properties.

Pure Bisphenol A is a white crystalline compound melting at 157°C. Commercial Bisphenol A may melt as low as 140°C; however, by temperature control, by maintaining a high phenol-to-acetone ratio, and by the use of catalysts,[16] it is possible under acidic conditions to get a very high yield of the 4,4′-dihydroxy compound:

$$2 \bigcirc \text{OH} + \text{COMe}_2 \longrightarrow \text{HO} \bigcirc \text{CMe}_2 \bigcirc \text{OH} + \text{H}_2\text{O}$$

6.2.2   MANUFACTURING PROCEDURE

There are two main methods for the preparation of polycarbonates, viz:

(i) Direct reaction of phosgene with dihydroxy compounds.

(ii) Transesterification (ester-interchange) between a dihydroxy compound and esters of carbonic acid.

6.2.2.1   *Direct Reaction with Phosgene*

A number of methods, all based on the classic Schotten-Baumann reaction, are possible. The simplest (passing phosgene into a solution of the bisphenol in alkali) gives only low molecular weight polymers since the growing polymer becomes insoluble in alkali. There are two principal variations of this method.

Emulsion Technique

This is really a pseudo-emulsion reaction. An aqueous alkali slurry of the bisphenol in an organic solvent is treated with phosgene in the presence of a catalytic amount of a quarternary base. It is thought that the growing polymer chain dissolves in the organic phase, while the active ionic ends remain in the aqueous caustic soda phase. Whatever the mechanism, this process gives a high molecular weight polymer, which can be recovered as a light fluffy powder. The removal of contaminating ionic material presents some problems, and the resulting material needs densifying.

Solvent Technique

A mixed-solvent system containing a tertiary amine such as pyridine is treated with phosgene. The amine functions as a hydrogen chloride acceptor. The solvent mixture can contain chloroform, methylene chloride, tetrachlorethane, and chlorinated benzenes. This mixture dissolves the bisphenol and the amine hydrochloride, and is also a partial solvent for the polymer. The polymer has to be washed free of ionic contaminants by means of water, either before or after it has been precipitated by addition of non-solvents; both methods are complicated on the large scale. Finally, the fluffy powder has to be densified.

6.2.2.2 *Transesterification*

A diaryl carbonate such as diphenyl carbonate is reacted in the molten state with the bisphenol. This entails high temperature, high vacuum, long reaction time, and the efficient mixing of high-viscosity melts. Temperatures up to 300°C and pressures as low as 1 mm are employed. The phenol liberated in the reaction can be reconverted to diphenyl carbonate. The polymer is forced out of

Table 6.1 ADVANTAGES AND DISADVANTAGES OF THE VARIOUS SYSTEMS FOR MAKING POLYCARBONATES

	Ester exchange	All-pyridine	Partial pyridine	Aqueous-inert solvent
ADVANTAGES	No solvents No solvent recovery Resins obtained in densified form	No molecular weight limitation Run under moderate conditions Simple equipment	No mol. wt. limitation Run under moderate conditions Simple equipment Lower cost solvents	No mol. wt. limitation Run under moderate conditions Simple equipment No costly solvents
DISADVANTAGES	Equipment limitations More difficult to get high mol. wts. High temp. and high vacuum with leak-proof operation necessary	Pyridine costly as solvent Very efficient solvent recovery necessary Polymer must be purified Polymer must be densified	Solvent recovery system needed At least three solvents must be recovered Polymer must be purified Polymer must be densified	Solvent recovery system needed At least two solvents must be recovered Polymer must be purified Polymer must be densified

the kettle under inert-gas pressure, in a form suitable for granulation to give the required end-product.

This method does not yield polymers of quite so high a molecular weight as does the solvent technique; but it has the advantage that no solvent-recovery is required.

6.2.2.3   *Summary*

Thompson and Goldblum[8] summarise the advantages and dis-advantages of these systems in Table 6.1.

The preferred method of production is by transesterification, using diphenyl carbonate as the source of the carbonate group. It avoids the use, and consequent recovery, of expensive solvents; and it yields a product in the desired state for use in extruders and injection machines.   Admittedly, dealing with the high viscosity of the polymer melt makes it difficult to obtain products of very high molecular weight, say above 30,000; but this is quite acceptable.

By using less than the theoretical amount of diphenyl carbonate, products of higher molecular weight can be obtained, but their colour is not so good, and the yield is poorer.

6.3   PROPERTIES

6.3.1   GENERAL

It is claimed[17] that polycarbonate resins based on Bisphenol A possess a combination of desirable properties unusual in thermo-plastics, and this is supported by information published by the three main manufacturers—General Electric Company (makers of Lexan), Mobay Chemical Company (makers of Merlon), and Farbenfabriken Bayer A.G. (makers of Makrolon).   Amongst the outstanding properties are high tensile allied with high impact strength, dimensional stability, thermal stability, optical clarity, and electrical resistance.   The properties in Tables 6.2–6.4 are quoted from trade literature.[18-20]   The values for the German material are based on D.I.N. test methods; those for American materials are based on A.S.T.M. methods, and are an average for the two materials, Lexan and Merlon.

6.3.1.1   *Mechanical Strength*

Table 6.2 shows the material to be one of the strongest and most rigid thermoplastics, and also to be unusually tough.

The ductility of the material does not show up in these figures, but reports show it to be ductile over a wide range of temperatures and rates of loading. When fracture takes place, it is accompanied by plastic flow. This is shown up clearly in tensile stress-strain curves, and more dramatically under impact test. Moulded parts have been known to withstand impact loads of greater than 120 ft/lb

Table 6.2

Property	D.I.N. Test Method and Units		A.S.T.M. Test Method and Units	
Specific gravity	53,479 g/cc	1·20	D.792	1·20
Tensile strength	53,455 kg/cm²	620–670	D.638 p.s.i.	8,000–10,500
Modulus of elasticity	kg/cm²	22,000–25,000	D.747 p.s.i.	28,000–32,000
Compressive strength	53,454 kg/am²	900–1,000	D.695 p.s.i.	11,500
Flexural strength	54,452 kg/cm²	1,100–1,200	D.790 p.s.i.	11,000–13,000
Impact strength (un-notched)	53,453 kg/cm²	100% not broken	D.256 ft. lb/in	60
Impact strength (notched)	53,453 kg/cm²	15–25	D.256 ft. lb/in of notch	12–16
Hardness	Brinell 10 sec	900–1,000	Rockwell	R–115
Elongation at break			D.638%	60–100

without cracking.[17] The thickness of the test-specimen is very significant in impact tests. An unnotched specimen up to $\frac{1}{4}$ in thick will withstand 60 ft lb/in, but notched test-pieces show quite different results. $\frac{1}{8}$ in thick specimens will give results of up to 16 ft lb/in of notch, but a specimen $\frac{1}{4}$ in thick will give results of only 2–3 ft/lb/in of notch.

6.3.1.2 *Dimensional Stability*

Polycarbonates are noted for their exceptionally good stability. This includes low deformation under load. A.S.T.M. test D.621 shows under 0·3% for loads up to 4,000 p.s.i. on a 0·5 in cube. Mould shrinkage is quite uniform at about 0·006 in per in, and is not accompanied by post-moulding shrinkage. Moulded articles have very low water-absorption characteristics, equilibrium conditions in fact show only about 0·5% on total immersion in boiling water. Since moulded articles demonstrate very little water pick-up in humid atmospheres, this means that they can be relied on to retain their moulded dimensions.

6.3.1.3 *Thermal Properties*

The heat distortion point (Table 6.3) is very high for a thermoplastic material. There is very little tendency to crystallise below the second-order transition point, and this gives excellent dimensional stability, even at sterilising temperatures. Moulded specimens will darken in colour when held near the maximum permissible service temperature for some months, but, with the exception of the elongation at break and the notched impact strength, the material does not show any great change in mechanical properties. Polycarbonate resins will burn under certain conditions, but are rated as self-extinguishing under the conditions of the A.S.T.M. test method D.635.

Melt-viscosity is obviously dependent on molecular weight, and unfortunately published results, which have indicated value of from 500,000 to 50,000 poises just above the melting range, have rarely recorded the molecular weight.

Table 6.3

Property	D.I.N. Test Method and Units		A.S.T.M. Test Method and Units	
Melting range	°C	222–230	°F	420–440
Heat-distortion point	53,456		D.648	
	Martens °C 57,302	115–127	°F at 264 p.s.i. D.648	270–280
	Vicat °C	164–166	°F at 66 p.s.i.	283–290
Thermal conductivity			cal/sec/ cm^2/°C/cm	4–6 × 10^{-4}
Specific heat		0·28		0·30
Coefficient of linear expansion	per °C	6 × 10^{-5}	in/in/°C	7 × 10^{-5}
Brittle point	°C	< − 100	D.746 °C	− 135
Second-order transition point	°C	140		
Maximum permissible service temperature	°C	135–137		

6.3.1.4 *Optical Clarity*

When made from pure Bisphenol A, the polycarbonate is transparent and nearly water-white, but commercial specimens, are light amber in colour. About 85% of visible light is transmitted through a sheet $\frac{1}{8}$ in thick. The refractive index is 1.586.

6.3.1.5 *Electrical Insulation*

The electrical properties (Table 6.4) are very useful, combining high dielectric strength and high resistivity with a dielectric constant which remains constant at about 3 over a wide range.

Table 6.4

Property	*D.I.N.* Test Method and Units		*A.S.T.M.* Test Method and Units	
Volume resistivity	53,482 ohm cm	4×10^{15}	D.257 ohm cm	9×10^{15}
Dielectric strength	53,481 kv/mm	100	D.149 v/mil.	400
Permittivity	53,483	3·0	D.150 at 60 cycles at 10^6 cycles	3·1 2·9
Power factor	53,483 at 50 cycles	5×10^{-4}	D.150 at 60 cycles at 10^6 cycles	7×10^{-4} 1×10^{-2}

6.3.1.6 *Other Properties*

Some additional properties of the material, such as solvent resistance, compatibility with other substances, and craze-resistance, show up certain of its limitations.

Chemical Properties

It is insoluble in water, ethyl alcohol, and light petroleum. It is stable in the presence of aliphatic hydrocarbons, dilute acids, and some alcohols, but is slowly attacked by alkaline solutions, amines, and concentrated mineral acids. It is easily soluble in chlorinated and some aromatic hydrocarbons, and partially soluble in ketones, and in aromatic hydrocarbons such as benzene and toluene.

Craze-resistance

Stressed specimens tend to craze in environments which have no effect on unstressed specimens. Christopher and Fox[21] have reported that a tensile strain of 0·75% (which corresponds to a loading of 2,000 p.s.i.) is the threshold limit, above which crazing will occur in air. In other environments, such as hydrocarbon vapours, moisture at elevated temperatures, soap solutions, and alkaline solutions, this threshold limit is lower.

6.4   PROCESSING AND APPLICATIONS

6.4.1   GENERAL

Ease of processing from the melt or from solution in conventional solvents allows polycarbonates to be processed by the usual methods. However, the high melt-viscosity of the Bisphenol A type, and the considerable degradation of the polymer in the molten state by traces of water, must be taken into consideration. This means that it is essential to work at high temperatures and with dry polymer.

6.4.1.1   *Injection Moulding*

For this, as for most other processes, the polycarbonate is supplied as pellets in a dry state packed in vacuum-sealed containers, and care must be taken to ensure that no moisture pick-up takes place before using. Moisture content should be kept below 0·03–0·05%. Probably the best way to do this is to heat the unopened tin in an oven at about 100–120°C for 4–6 hours. This does not dry the resin (it is already dry), but it produces hot pellets which do not then pick up moisture. Pellets can be preheated on trays in an oven; but this is not advised, as the heated air in the oven contains some moisture, and an equilibrium is set up, which leaves the polymer with an appreciable amount of water. If the preheating air is not passed through a dehumidifying chamber, the minimum temperature needed to keep the moisture content below 0·03% depends on the humidity of the air. For example, at 80% R.H. (room temperature), a preheat temperature of 125°C is needed to ensure this result.

After preheat, the pellets are loaded into the hopper, which should have a tight-fitting lid to exclude room air, or should have a heating device to keep it at about 110–120°C. Cold pellets with a hot-air circulating hopper are not safe, as this system may actually result in moisture pick-up by the pellets.

All types of injection-moulding machines can be used, provided that they have sufficient heating capacity to provide a uniform melt, and that they can produce sufficient pressure to overcome the high melt-viscosity. Melt-temperatures of from 240° to 300°C, and pressures of from 14,000 to 20,000 p.s.i., are recommended for plunger machines. Lower pressures can obviously be used on pre-plasticising types. The mould itself should be channelled for heating, and should be kept between 85° and 125°C.

6.4.1.2 *Extrusion Moulding*

Suitable extruders should have a L : D ratio of from 15 : 1 upwards, and a compression ratio between 2 : 1 and 4 : 1. The high melt-viscosity of the resin influences the mesh-size of the screen-packs used. In general, large mesh is all that is needed to ensure adequate back-pressure and plasticisation. A uniform heat-profile along the extruder gives good results. Suitable temperatures are around 285°C.

Only limited information is available on the extrusion of poly-carbonates. This has been summarised by Fielder[17] in the 1962 edition of *Modern Plastics Encyclopedia*, and it is reasonable to assume that new developments will be reported in subsequent editions.

6.4.1.3 *Blow Moulding*

Here again only limited information is available. A supplier[22] recommends either a heart-curve mandrel or a ring-groove mandrel for forming the parison or blow-tube. Because of the high second-order transition point, moulds can be run at very high temperatures. However, a compromise has to be met between processing time, blowing pressure, quality of bottle produced, and overall economical manufacture. A useful compromise is to run the mould between 40° and 60°C.

6.4.1.4 *Solvent Casting and Extruding of Film*

Since the polymer is soluble in chlorinated aliphatic hydrocarbons, film can be produced by standard methods. Films can also be produced by extruding through a slit die, or by blowing an extruded tube.

6.4.1.5 *Machining*

The mouldings can be machined using standard metal-working tools, as the polymer is rigid, ductile, and of high melting point. Parts may be turned, shaped, milled, routed, drilled, planed, sawed, cut, punched, and sheared with ease. The only limitation is that, with some operations, rapid heavy cuts can produce surface strains, which may require to be relieved by annealing.

6.4.2 APPLICATIONS

Polycarbonates are still relatively expensive, and so find their chief applications in fields where their valuable properties offset this disadvantage.   The foregoing account will have shown that these properties are as follows:

1. Good mechanical strength (especially impact strength) over a wide temperature range.
2. Excellent dimensional stability, and accuracy of moulding to close tolerances.
3. Good electrical properties which do not vary greatly up to 140°C.
4. Low water-absorption.
5. Good weather-resistance.
6. Transparency.

However, the limitations are poor solvent- and chemical-resistance, and inability to withstand even moderate stresses in certain circumstances.   The balance of properties has resulted in the following applications for this new polymer:

1. Mechanical applications which call for strength, stiffness, impact resistance, and dimensional stability.
2. Electrical applications which have to withstand difficult operating conditions calling for high temperature-resistance, self-extinguishing properties, and toughness.
3. Applications calling for transparency in addition to heat-resistance, toughness, and high dimensional-stability.
4. Dynamic applications which entail only light loadings.
5. Film with excellent dimensional stability, high strength, and thermal stability combined with good optical properties.
6. Household utensils, which demand an attractive, unbreakable, easy-to-clean material.

REFERENCES

(1) EINHORN, A., *Ann. Chem.*, **300**, 135 (1898)
(2) BISCHOFF, C. A., and HEDENSTRÖM, A. V., *Ber.*, **35**, 3431 (1902)
(3) CAROTHERS, W. H., and NATTA, F. J., *J. Amer. Chem. Soc.*, **52**, 314 (1930)
(4) SCHNELL, H., *Angew. Chem.*, **68**, 633 (1956)
(5) REMOND, J., *Rev. Prod. Chim.*, **305** & **381** (1957)
(6) SCHNELL, H., *Plast. Inst. Trans.*, **28**, 143 (1960)

(7) COTTIN, G., *Chim. Moderne*, **19**, 183 (1958)
(8) THOMPSON, R. J., and GOLDBLUM, K. B., *Mod. Plast.*, **35**, 131 (1958)
(9) Farbenfabriken Bayer A.G., Brit. Pat. 857,430
(10) Farbenfabriken Bayer A.G., Brit. Pat. 808,485
(11) Farbenfabriken Bayer A.G., Brit. Pat. 842,759
(12) Badische Anilin & Soda-Fabrik A.G., Brit. Pat. 843,314
(13) Beiersdorf A.G., Brit. Pat. 846,004
(14) *Mod. Plast.*, **39**, 95 (1962)
(15) DIANIN, A., *J. Russ. Phys-Chem. Soc.*, **23**, 488, 523, 601 (1891)
(16) U.S. PATENT 2,468,982
(17) FIELDER, E. F., *Mod. Plast. Ency.*, **40**, 253 (1962)
(18) General Electric Co., *Tech. Bulletin* 157
(19) Mobay Products Co., *Inf. Sheet T.I.B.* 41–M1
(20) Farbenfabriken Bayer, A.G., *Bulletin 1159*
(21) CHRISTOPHER, W. F., and FOX, D. W., *Polycarbonates* (Reinhold, 1962)
(22) R. H. COLE & CO. LTD., Blow Moulding Makrolon: *Data Sheet No. 30*

PATENTS ON PRODUCTION

N.V. Onderzoekings Institut Research, Brit. Pats. 843,881; 861,918
General Electric Co., Brit. Pats. 835,464; 835,465; 820,603
Columbia Southern Chem. Corp., Brit. Pats. 828,523; 828,525; 820,603
Farbenfabriken Bayer A.G., Brit. Pats. 800,815; 808,486–808,490; 809,735; 811,628; 824,423
Eastman Kodak Co., U.S. Pats. 2,789,964–2,789,971

INDEX